IT'S A WONDERFUL WIFE

Welcome tae this really remarkable book. It is very braw tae be in full 'technicolour' for the first time in the history of The Broons! Whether it's Paw feeling blue efter Auchentogle Rovers get beaten again or Daphne being red-faced at the state o' her latest boyfriend, ye'll get tae see us as we see oorsels. There's an added bonus for Broons fans here tae – now we're in colour you'll learn my secret how I tell Ae twin frae the Ither.

Ae twin has yellow hair while the Ither is a ginger!

Me and Wee Harry are so happy at bein' in colour for the first time that we've decided tae dance a wee jig! Mak the most o' it as it only happens once in a blue moon! Want tae ken the best thing aboot being in colour? Well, tartan's in black and white a' look the same – like the table cloths in Toni's chipper – so it's braw seein' my ain special tartan in a' its glory. It's a belter, richt enough.

OOR WULLIE YOUR WULLIE A'BODY'S WULLIE

MOVIE MAGIC!

IT'S FAIR TAE SAY I'M SOMETHING O' A MOVIE BUFF AN' I'VE WATCHED HUNNERS AND HUNNERS O' FILMS! JOE SAYS I GO INTO IT ALL FAR TOO DEEPLY AND THAT I COULD EVEN TELL YE THE NAME O' THE TYPE OF AEROPLANE THEY USED IN THE FINAL SCENE O' THE CLASSIC 1942 FILM, CASABLANCA! WELL, SO WHAT IF I KNOW THAT IT WAS A LOCKHEED MODEL 12 ELECTRA JUNIOR? WE ALL NEED A HOBBY AND I RECKON HE SHOULD SPEND LESS TIME WINCHING IN THE BACK ROW O' THE MULTIPLEX AND MAIR TIME PAYIN' ATTENTION TAE WHAT'S OAN THE SCREEN!

TO THOSE OF YE WHA THINK LIKE ME, I'VE PUT AN APPROPRIATE MOVIE TITLE TAE EIGHTY-FIVE O' THE STORIES IN THIS BOOK AND I'VE ALSO ADDED THE YEAR IN WHICH THEY WERE RELEASED. I'VE WATCHED EVERY SINGLE ANE O' THE ORIGINALS - HOW MANY CAN YOU CLAIM TAE HAE SEEN?

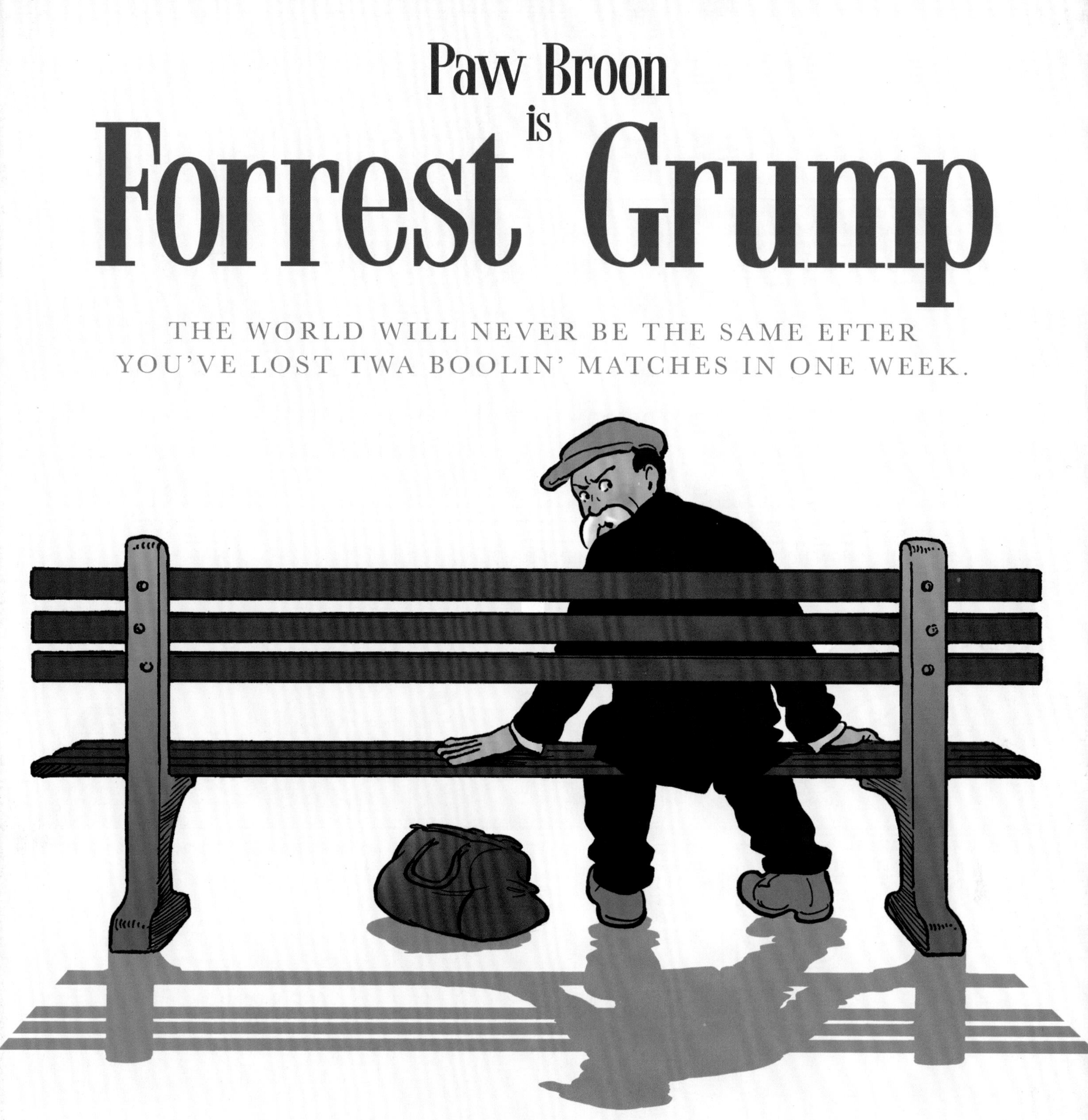

Paw Broon
is
Forrest Grump
THE WORLD WILL NEVER BE THE SAME EFTER
YOU'VE LOST TWA BOOLIN' MATCHES IN ONE WEEK.

—FILMED AT—

AUCHENTOGLE BOOLIN' CLUB

BEFORE THE FIGHT BROKE OUT.

— LATER AT —

GLEBE STREET POLIS STATION.

MR BROON APPEARS COURTESY OF MRS BROON WHO HAS LET HIM OUT THE DOGHOUSE.

—BUNNET BY—

CASUAL CAPS OF GLENTOORIE.

—MAKE-UP TAE HIDE THE BRUISES BY—

MAGGIE BROON.

OOR WULLIE
in "Circus Days!"
(Original movie 1923)
JUST BEEN WATCHING CIRCUS JUGGLERS ON THE TELLY... I THINK I'LL GIE IT A BASH.
I'LL START WI' SOMETHING BIG AND EASY... MY BUCKET AND FITBA'... HUP!
CLANG!
HOWL!
BONK!
BRAW HEIDER, WULLIE. HA! HA!
OCHT!
HOW NO' TRY HARD-BOILED EGGS?
GUID IDEA!
NAE PROBS!
ACH! THESE ARE NO' HARD BOILED AT A'!
SPLOT!
SPLAT!
NEVER SAID THEY WERE! WAIT 'TIL MY MA FINDS OOT!
SPLAT!
SPLOT!
JUGGLERS SOMETIMES USE CLUBS... HMM...
THE ONLY CLUBS I CAN FIND ARE PA'S GOLF ANES...
WULLIE!
...AND THEY'RE NO' MUCKLE USE! JINGS! I'M AFF!
CLUNK!
FISH
CHIPS
PEAS
PIES
OCH! GIE UP, WULLIE! YE CANNA JUGGLE FOR MINCE! I'M GONNA HAE A BAG O' CHIPS TAE CHEER MASEL' UP!
SHUFFLE!
CRIVVENS! YON CHIPS ARE HOT!
HA! HA! JUGGLIN' HOT CHIPS IS NAE BOTHER TAE ME! DOON THE HATCH!
KEN. H. HARRISON

THE BROONS in "Slipstream!"
(Original movie 1989)
OOR TWINS HAVE BUILT A SLIDE RICHT OOTSIDE OOR CLOSE... MAKIN' ME FALL... LOOK AT THE STATE O' MY BEST STOCKINGS!
ME AN' A'! LOOK AT THE MESSAGES!
NAE HARM IN IT...
BUT...
YE'D BETTER SALT IT, PAW.
AYE! IT'S OWER DANGEROUS.
SALT
I USED TAE LET YOU HAE SLIDES WHEN YOU WERE A YOUNG LAD.
DINNA MIND O' THAT.
RICHT YOU TWA, I'VE COME TAE SALT YER SLIDE... OWER DANGEROUS.
OCH! PAW!
HELP MA BOAB! I'M ON THE SLIDE ALREADY!
HAW! HAW!
SKITE!
BUT SHORTLY...
THERE! SALTED!
ACH! AULD GOWK!
DINNA YOU TWINS MIND... I KNOW A MUCH BETTER PLACE TAE SLIDE... JOCK'S BRAE!
LET'S GO!
AND SO...
BUT, AT JOCK'S BRAE...
YE TWA FACED...
OCH! YE BROCHT BACK BRAW MEMORIES WHEN YE 'MINDED ME O' ME SLIDIN'...
YIPPEE! NO' HAD SO MUCH FUN IN AGES!
AYE! SLIDING'S A'RICHT IN THE RICHT PLACE! WHA'S FOR HOT SOUP?
KEN.H. HARRISON.

OOR WULLIE in "The Guard!"
(Original movie 2011)
I'M ON GUARD THE DAY . . .
. . . BECAUSE PA'S RASPS ARE MUCH SOUGHT EFTER ROOND HERE!
WI' ME ON GUARD, NAEBODY'LL GET A LOOK-IN!
AN' I'VE GOT MY TRUSTY LIEUTENANTS TAE HELP ME — HARRY . . .
. . . AN' JEEMY, THE LOOK-OOT MOOSE!
GO ON, WULLIE — JIST ONE RASPBERRY! YER PA'LL NEVER KEN!
NAE CHANCE! I GAVE MY WORD AS A LADDIE O' HONOUR!
THAT'S THEM TELT!
HUH! WHAT'RE PALS FOR, IF NO' TAE FEED YE THEIR PA'S RASPBERRIES?
BUT THEN . . .
MY, YER PA'S RASPS LOOK GREAT, WULLIE! ONY CHANCE O' A COUPLE?
OH! ER . . . WEEL . . . AS IT'S YOU, MAGGIE . . . I S'POSE . . .
WE HEARD THAT!
IT'S FAVOURITISM FOR BONNY LASSIES! WE SHOULD GET A COUPLE, AN' A'!
OCH!!
SORRY — IF YE ALL GOT A COUPLE, THERE'D BE NANE LEFT AT A'!
HAH! REPELLED ALL BOARDERS, NAE PROBLEM!
THEN . . .
HEY! SOMEBODY'S SNEAKED IN WHILE MY BACK WAS TURNED!
RUSTLE!
MA!
OCH! CAUGHT! DINNAE TELL PA, WULLIE — BUT HE USUALLY TAK'S THEM A' FOR HIS BLOOMIN' HORTICULTURAL SHOWS!
WEEL, IF YE CANNAE BEAT THEM, JOIN THEM, I SAY! BRAW!
FUNNY! THEY'VE A' DISAPPEARED!
SO HAS WULLIE! IN BED WI' A SAIR STOMACH!
KEN.H. HARRISON.

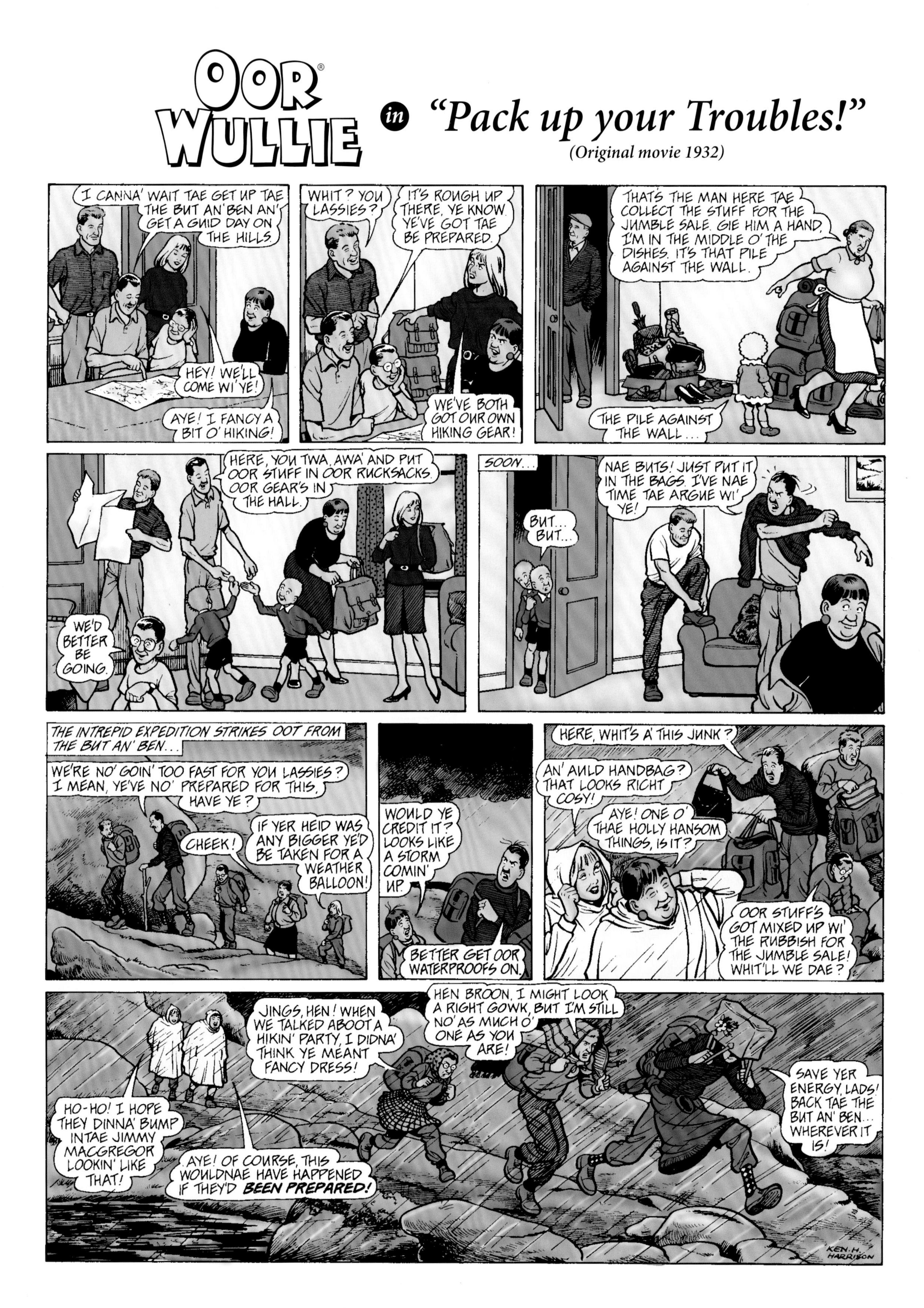
OOR WULLIE
in "Pack up your Troubles!"
(Original movie 1932)
I CANNA' WAIT TAE GET UP TAE THE BUT AN' BEN AN' GET A GUID DAY ON THE HILLS.
HEY! WE'LL COME WI' YE!
AYE! I FANCY A BIT O' HIKING!
WHIT? YOU LASSIES?
IT'S ROUGH UP THERE, YE KNOW. YE'VE GOT TAE BE PREPARED.
WE'VE BOTH GOT OUR OWN HIKING GEAR!
THAT'S THE MAN HERE TAE COLLECT THE STUFF FOR THE JUMBLE SALE. GIE HIM A HAND, I'M IN THE MIDDLE O' THE DISHES. IT'S THAT PILE AGAINST THE WALL.
THE PILE AGAINST THE WALL...
HERE, YOU TWA, AWA' AND PUT OOR STUFF IN OOR RUCKSACKS. OOR GEAR'S IN THE HALL.
WE'D BETTER BE GOING.
SOON...
BUT... BUT...
NAE BUTS! JUST PUT IT IN THE BAGS. I'VE NAE TIME TAE ARGUE WI' YE!
THE INTREPID EXPEDITION STRIKES OOT FROM THE BUT AN' BEN...
WE'RE NO' GOIN' TOO FAST FOR YOU LASSIES? I MEAN, YE'VE NO' PREPARED FOR THIS, HAVE YE?
CHEEK!
IF YER HEID WAS ANY BIGGER YE'D BE TAKEN FOR A WEATHER BALLOON!
WOULD YE CREDIT IT? LOOKS LIKE A STORM COMIN' UP.
BETTER GET OOR WATERPROOFS ON.
HERE, WHIT'S A' THIS JUNK?
AN' AULD HANDBAG? THAT LOOKS RICHT COSY!
AYE! ONE O' THAE HOLLY HANSOM THINGS, IS IT?
OOR STUFF'S GOT MIXED UP WI' THE RUBBISH FOR THE JUMBLE SALE! WHIT'LL WE DAE?
HO-HO! I HOPE THEY DINNA' BUMP INTAE JIMMY MACGREGOR LOOKIN' LIKE THAT!
AYE! OF COURSE, THIS WOULDNAE HAVE HAPPENED IF THEY'D **BEEN PREPARED!**
JINGS, HEN! WHEN WE TALKED ABOOT A HIKIN' PARTY, I DIDNA' THINK YE MEANT FANCY DRESS!
HEN BROON, I MIGHT LOOK A RIGHT GOWK, BUT I'M STILL NO' AS MUCH O' ONE AS YOU ARE!
SAVE YER ENERGY, LADS! BACK TAE THE BUT AN' BEN... WHEREVER IT IS!
KEN. H. HARRISON

OOR® WULLIE
in "Not Easily Broken!"
(Original movie 2009)
CONKER CHAMPIONSHIPS TIME O' YEAR.
AH'VE GOT A CHAMP. A NINETY-SEVENSER.
OH, AYE? LET'S SEE IT THEN.
HAW! HAW! THON A CHAMP? NAE CHANCE!
WE'LL SEE.
TELL YE WHAT, BOB. YE CAN HAE FIRST WHACK AT MY TENSER.
IF YE INSIST.
NINETY-EIGHT!
WHIT?
JIST TRY THAT OAN MY TWENTY-ONESER!
RICHT! I WILL.
NINETY-NINE!
JINGS!
A'RICHT! YE'LL NO' BEAT MY FORTY-NINER! AN' AH'M GOIN' FIRST!
PLEASE YERSEL'.
CRIVVENS!
ONE HUNDRED-NOT OOT!
HEE! HEE! NEXT!
GRR! SOMETHING FISHY'S GOIN' ON HERE.
SOON-
HAUD IT! AH'M THE OFFISHUL CONKER INSPECTOR COME TAE MAK' AN INSPECTION.
AYE, OKAY. THEY'RE IN THE CLEAR. NEXT ANE!
OO-ER!
AS I THOCHT, IT'S METAL!
ULP!
CHINK!
FAT BOB, YE'RE HEREBY BANNED SINE DIE FRAE THE CONKER CHAMPIONSHIPS!
OCH!
HE'S PAINTED AN AULD BALL-BEARING! CHEATIN' DOG!
OOR WULLIE CONKERS AGAIN! HA! HA!
KEN. H. HARRISON.

THE BROONS
in "The Game!"
(Original movie 1997)
DAE YE NO' WANT YER DINNER, YOU THREE?
WE'VE NAE TIME, MAW! WE'RE LATE FOR THE BIG MATCH. WE'LL MAYBE GRAB SOMETHING ON THE WAY.
ACH! YOU YOUNG ANES ARE ALWAYS RUSHIN' ABOOT! I'LL CATCH YE UP LATER.
BUS STOP
FISH 'N' CH
HEY! THERE'S A CHIPPER! WE COULD NIP IN AFORE THE BUS ARRIVES.
MICHTY! THE BUS IS AWA'! HAUD IT, MISSUS!
I SAID THAT QUEUE WAS OWER LANG!
JINGS! GOT TAE HURRY!
OCH! WE'VE GOT TAE THE GROUND OWER EARLY AFTER A' THAT RUSH!
I'M STILL HUNGRY, PAW. LET'S GET A BURGER!
BURGER BA
UNITED V ROVE
E
D
THERE'S PLENTY O' TIME TAE HAE A WEE REST AFORE THE GAME STARTS.
AYE, I'M FAIR PUGGLED MYSEL'!
MAN, THAT WAS GRAND!
PHEEP!
WHIT! THAT MUST BE THE WHISTLE F'R THE START O' THE MATCH!
AW, JINGS! THAT WAS THE FINAL WHISTLE! WE'VE SLEPT THROUGH THE WHOLE GAME!
HO-HO! THAT'S WHIT YE CALL A SLEEPIN' SUPPORT!
STILL OOT FOR THE COUNT!
DAFT GOWK! NEVER MIND, YE DIDNA' MISS MUCH – IT WAS A GOALLESS DRAW.
The Sunday Post
KEN. H. HARRISON.

"Bathing Beauty!"

(Original movie 1944)

DROOKIT' IN THE RAIN

WHAT A GOD-AWFUL FEELING,

WE'RE SOAKING AGAIN!

Early scenes, The Broons and Oor Wullie during the war years.

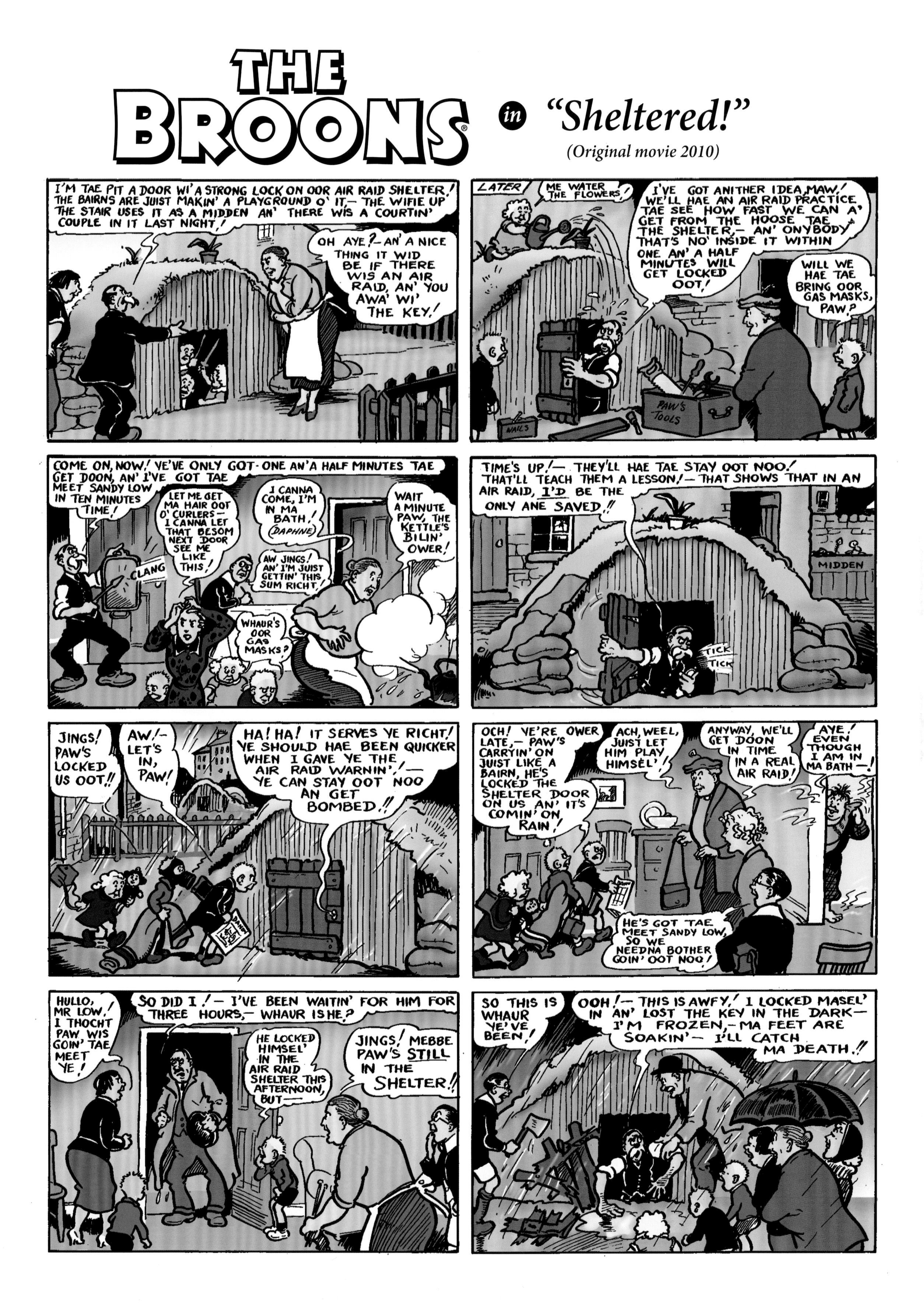
THE BROONS
in "Sheltered!"
(Original movie 2010)
I'M TAE PIT A DOOR WI' A STRONG LOCK ON OOR AIR RAID SHELTER! THE BAIRNS ARE JUIST MAKIN' A PLAYGROUND O' IT,— THE WIFIE UP THE STAIR USES IT AS A MIDDEN AN' THERE WIS A COURTIN' COUPLE IN IT LAST NIGHT!
OH AYE?— AN' A NICE THING IT WID BE IF THERE WIS AN AIR RAID, AN' YOU AWA' WI' THE KEY!
LATER
ME WATER THE FLOWERS!
I'VE GOT ANITHER IDEA, MAW! WE'LL HAE AN AIR RAID PRACTICE TAE SEE HOW FAST WE CAN A' GET FROM THE HOOSE TAE THE SHELTER,— AN' ONYBODY THAT'S NO' INSIDE IT WITHIN ONE AN' A HALF MINUTES WILL GET LOCKED OOT!
WILL WE HAE TAE BRING OOR GAS MASKS, PAW?
PAW'S TOOLS
NAILS
COME ON, NOW! YE'VE ONLY GOT ONE AN' A HALF MINUTES TAE GET DOON, AN' I'VE GOT TAE MEET SANDY LOW IN TEN MINUTES TIME!
LET ME GET MA HAIR OOT O' CURLERS— I CANNA LET THAT BESOM NEXT DOOR SEE ME LIKE THIS!
I CANNA COME, I'M IN MA BATH! (DAPHNE)
WAIT A MINUTE PAW, THE KETTLE'S BILIN' OWER!
CLANG
AW JINGS! AN' I'M JUIST GETTIN' THIS SUM RICHT!
WHAUR'S OOR GAS MASKS?
TIME'S UP!— THEY'LL HAE TAE STAY OOT NOO! THAT'LL TEACH THEM A LESSON!— THAT SHOWS THAT IN AN AIR RAID, I'D BE THE ONLY ANE SAVED!!
MIDDEN
TICK
TICK
JINGS! PAW'S LOCKED US OOT!!
AW!— LET'S IN, PAW!
HA! HA! IT SERVES YE RICHT! YE SHOULD HAE BEEN QUICKER WHEN I GAVE YE THE AIR RAID WARNIN'!— YE CAN STAY OOT NOO AN GET BOMBED!!
OCH! YE'RE OWER LATE,— PAW'S CARRYIN' ON JUIST LIKE A BAIRN, HE'S LOCKED THE SHELTER DOOR ON US AN' IT'S COMIN' ON RAIN!
ACH, WEEL, JUIST LET HIM PLAY HIMSEL'!
ANYWAY, WE'LL GET DOON IN TIME IN A REAL AIR RAID!
AYE! EVEN THOUGH I AM IN MA BATH—!
HE'S GOT TAE MEET SANDY LOW, SO WE NEEDNA BOTHER GOIN' OOT NOO!
HULLO, MR LOW! I THOCHT PAW WIS GOIN' TAE MEET YE!
SO DID I!— I'VE BEEN WAITIN' FOR HIM FOR THREE HOURS,— WHAUR IS HE?
HE LOCKED HIMSEL' IN THE AIR RAID SHELTER THIS AFTERNOON, BUT—
JINGS! MEBBE PAW'S STILL IN THE SHELTER!!
SO THIS IS WHAUR YE'VE BEEN!
OOH!— THIS IS AWFY! I LOCKED MASEL' IN AN' LOST THE KEY IN THE DARK— I'M FROZEN,— MA FEET ARE SOAKIN'— I'LL CATCH MA DEATH!!

in "Guess Who's Coming to Dinner?!"

(Original movie 1967)

THE BROONS
in "Fit for a King!"
(Original movie 1937)

THE STRENGTH, ENDURANCE AND STAMINA OF OUR BRITISH FIGHTING MEN
JINGS! THAT LAD KENS WHIT HE'S TALKIN' ABOOT! IT WIS OOR STRENGTH AN' ENDURANCE THAT WON US THE LAST WAR!
AYE, AN' THE BOER WAR, TOO! I MIND FINE FOR A WEEK LIVIN' ON STEWED HORSES! I BET WE COULD DAE IT YET!
AW! DINNA MAK' ME LAUGH! YE'RE NO' EVEN TOUGH ENOUGH TAE GO TAE BED WI'OOT A HOT WATER BOTTLE!
AYE, YE'VE GOT TAE BE TOUGH IN THE ARMY! I'D LIKE TAE SEE DAPHNE HUMPIN' A PACK ON A TWENTY MILE ROUTE MARCH LIKE WE'RE DAEIN' THE MORN!
OR GOIN' ROOND A' DAY TESTIN' GAS MASKS, THEN SPENDIN' THE NICHT AT THE WARDENS' POST!
HUH! HOT-WATER BOTTLES, EH? I'M NO' SPEAKIN' TAE YE!
HEN ON HIS ROUTE MARCH
THINKS:— ONE MORE MILE TAE GO! JINGS! THIS HAS BEEN MURDER! MICHTY ME,-I'M GLAD IT'S SATURDAY THE MORN, I'LL GET A NICE QUIET WEEK END AT HAME!
YE KEN, JOCK, THAT CORPORAL BROON'S A NARK!
THIS BLOOMIN' BATTLE PRACTICE GIES ME A PAIN!- WHIT A LIFE,— STILL IT'S SATURDAY THE MORN, I'LL BE ABLE TAE GET A REST AT HAME!
HULLO, BROON! WHIT ARE YE CRIPPLIN' FOR?
AW JINGS! I'VE BEEN ROOND ON MA WARDEN'S DUTIES, AN' MA FEET ARE A' BLISTERS!
AYE,- IT'S GAUN TAE RAIN, MA CORNS ARE GIVIN' ME WHAT-HO!
TENDER
NEXT DAY
WE'VE HAD A STRENUOUS WEEK, YOU YINS! IT'S TIME WE HAD A REST!
I'M JUIST GAUN TAE SIT IN THE EASY CHAIR TILL MONDAY!
AN' I'LL GANG TAE MA BED FOR THE WEEK END!
The Broon's Clossie
HULLO! WHIT ARE YE A' DRESSED UP LIKE HIKERS FOR?
OH, WE DECIDED IT WIS TIME WE TOUGHENED OORSEL'S UP A BIT AN' MADE OORSEL'S WORTHY O' OOR MENFOLK! SO WE'RE GAUN HIKIN' WITH YOU THIS AFTERNOON!
AN' AS YOU HE-MEN ARE SO MUCH TOUGHER THAN US YOU CAN CARRY THE FOOD!
WE'LL HAE TAE DAE A LOT O' WALKIN' TAE MAK' OORSEL'S TOUGH LIKE HEN, JOE, PAW AN' GRAN'PAW!
AYE! IT'LL SOON BE OOR CALLIN' UP AGE!
GRAN'PAW'S NO' REALLY TOUGH! HE'S JUIST AN AULD HAVER!
MY! I'M PROUD TAE BE OOT HIKIN' WI' MA BRAW SOJER SONS, AN' THEM SAE TOUGH!
THOUGHT
WHAT MIGHT HAVE BEEN
DAY-DREAM
OH! WHY EVER DID WE SAY WE WIS TOUGH!
AN' HOO DID YOU HAE TAE START BOASTIN' ABOOT THE BOER WAR?
I THOCHT YE SAID YE WIS TOUGH, JOE!
TENDER

THE BROONS
in "The Quarrel!"
(Original movie 1991)

WHERE'S MA BLACK-POINTED HAT! I WANT IT TAE GO AN' HAE MA PHOTIE TAKEN! COME ON, MAGGIE— YOU MUST HAVE SEEN IT!
I HAVE NOT! I'VE TIDIED UP THE WARDROBE AN' OOR ROOM AN' NEVER SAW IT. BUT I FOUND MAW'S HAT IN OOR ROOM, THOUGH SHE NEVER PITS IT THERE!
DINNA YOU BLAME MAGGIE! IT'S LIKELY YER AIN CARELESSNESS!
IT'S AN AWFY LOOKIN' THING, ONYWAY— THON HAT!
THAT'S WHIT YOU THINK! — I'VE BEEN COMPLIMENTED ON IT!
HULLO! WHIT'S GAUN ON?
YOU LEAVE OOR SISTER ALANE, YE FOUR-EYED TWERP!
YOU TWINS ARE JUIST A PAIR O' SCRUFFY WEE RAGTAGS!
HUH! COME ON AN' FECHT THE TWA O' US, THEN, YE COWARD!
WHIT? IS IT YER BONNY HAT YE'VE LOST, DAPHNE? AYE, I BET MAGGIE'S PITTEN IT IN THE FIRE— SHE'S THAT JEALOUS O' IT!
WEEL, THAT'S THE BEST PLACE FOR IT, SHE LOOKS DAFT ENOUGH WI'OOT WEARIN' A RABBIT-EARED HAT LIKE YON!
SHE'S ACCUSIN' ME O' LOSIN' HER HAT,— AS IF I WID BE SEEN DEAD WI' IT!
COME ON, YE BIG GOWK!
OUCH!!
HIT HIM, ECK!
PUIR DAPHNE! IS MAGGIE BEIN' NASTY TAE YE?
YE-YE- RATTLESNAKE!!
YOU— HORRID BESOM!!
HUH! WHIT DAE YOU KEN ABOOT WOMEN'S HATS?—YE BIG JESS!!
CA' ME A BIG JESS, WID YE— COME ON OOTSIDE AN' I'LL BASH YE!
HEY, YOU— GRAN'PAW! YOU KEEP YER NOSE OOT, YOU LEAVE MY MAGGIE ALANE!
NOW! NOW! FOLKS! I DINNA LIKE TAE SEE THIS AWFY QUARRELLIN' GAUN ON, DISTURBIN' THE PEACE O' THE HAME! REMEMBER THERE'S A WAR ON,—WE'VE A' GOT TAE PULL TAEGETHER!
CAT!!
BESOM!!
FORBYE, CELTIC PLAY BETTER FITBA' THAN RANGERS!
WHIT! DINNA BE DAFT! LET ME TELL YOU—!
YOU JUIST AN AULD FOGEY TODDLER!
WE'VE GOT HIM NOW!
AH'M A— WHIT DID YE CA' ME?
SCRAM!!— THIS IS OOR ARGUMENT— GET OOT O' THIS!
LIKE ENOUGH IT WIS PAW THAT PINCHED YER HAT, DAPHNE!
AYE!— PIT IT IN HIS PIPE, THINKIN' IT WIS THICK TWIST!
HEY! WE DINNA WANT NANE O' YOUR SERMONS, PAW!
CAN ME AN' GRAN'PAW NO' GET LEAVE TAE FECHT IN PEACE?
CAN YE NO LEAVE US ALANE, PAW? WE'VE JUIST GOT HORACE TAE CRY FOR MERCY!
JINGS! LOOK!! — MAW'S GOT YER HAT ON, DAPHNE!
NOO WID YE CREDIT THAT!!
WEEL, I HAD TAE GANG A MESSAGE IN A HURRY AN' AS I COULDNA SEE MA AIN HAT I JUIST LIFTED YOURS, DAPHNE!
I'LL JUIST GIE YER NOSE A DAB O' MA NEW POWDER,— YE'RE LOOKIN' REAL NICE!!
THEY SAY I'M AWFY NATURAL LIKE WI' THIS HAT!
I'LL ADMIT RANGERS IS A GRAND TEAM!— THEY'VE GOT STYLE AN' POLISH!
AYE! AN' CELTIC HAVE GOT THE CRAFT!
WHIT ABOOT US GAUN TAE THE PICTERS, MA WEE LAMB!
O.K. CHUM!
I'LL READ YE A COWBOY STORY!

THE BROONS in "Dirty Laundry!"

(Original movie 1987)

THE BROONS
in "Pie in the Sky!"
(Original movie 1996)

HEY! THE TABLE'S NO LAID FOR THE TEA YET!
JINGS! A STEAK PIE! OH BOY! HURRY WI' THE TEA, MAW! WE'RE BAITH STARVIN' AN' READY TAE GET OOR TEETH INTO THAT BRAW PIE!
YE'LL HAE TAE MAK YER AIN TEA, AN' FORBYE, THAT PIE IS FOR THE PARTY! ME AN' THE LASSIES ARE HELPIN' THE NICHT IN THE MASONS' HALL!
WE'RE GOIN' DOON THERE NOW, AN' THE PIE IS FOR THE SODGERS!
AH WEEL, YE'LL NO' GET ME TAE COME TAE YER PAIRTY AN' TAK' YE HAME!!
YE CANNA COME ANYHOW! IT'S FOR FOLKS IN UNIFORM ONLY, SO THERE!
WE WIDNA BE SEEN DEAD AT YER PAIRTY! WE'LL HAE A RARE NICHT AT HAME,— ME AN' GRAN'PAW AN' A' THE BOYS PLAYIN' DOMINOES!
BUT WE'RE A' GAUN TAE THE PAIRTY!
NO COSY
JUIST LIKE WOMEN, AWA' GALLIVANTIN' AN' LEAVIN' US AT HAME TAE WASH A' OOR TEA DISHES!
HERE! I THINK I KEN HOO TAE GET INTO THE PAIRTY— WE'LL MAK' OOR AIN UNIFORMS OOT O' YON AULD UNIFORMS AT YOUR PLACE!
WASHIN' UP— TWA CUPPIES AND A KNIFE
AT GRAN'PAW'S
HERE'S A RARE SUN HELMET I HAD IN SOUTH AFRICA!
AT THE MASONS' HALL
KITCHEN
OH! MORE MEN IN UNIFORM— COME IN, WHAT REGIMENT ARE YOU IN?
WE'VE COME TO THE PARTY, MISS, AND WE'RE OFFICERS IN THE CALCUTTA HORSE MARINES!
WOULD YOU LIKE A BITE OF SUPPER?
I-AH-WOULDN'T MIND A BITE OF THAT— AH-PIE, WHAT!
JINGS! IF MAW KEN'T— IT'S HER STEAK PIE!!
BE QUICK AN' GIE'S A BIT!
YES, TWO NICE OFFICERS,— FROM INDIA, I THINK!
OH, I MUST MEET THEM!
CRIVVENS! MICHTY ME!! OFFICERS MA FOOT! GET OOT O' THIS—YE AULD FRAUDS!!!
OUT YOU GO!!
I'M ASHAMED O' THEM— TAKIN' US DOON LIKE THIS!
TUT-TUT!
TRIPPING OWER HIS SWORD
MASONS HALL
LEAVE IT TAE ME, LAD— I CAPTURED THE PIE!!

in *“The Recruit!”*

(Original movie 2003)

in "The Job!"

(Original movie 2009)

MAW BROON
PAW BROON

Starring in

Auchentogle

THE BROONS
in "True Romance!"
(Original movie 1993)
MONDAY EVENING
GRACIOUS! LOOK AT OOR DAPHNE WI' A LAD!
HE LOOKS A DECENT LIKE CHAP!
JINGS! SHE NEVER TELT ME SHE HAD A CLICK!
CINEMA
TUESDAY
JINGS! THERE'S DAPHNE AN' THON LAD AGAIN!
SHE LOOKS LIKE SHE'S GOIN' STEADY WI' HIM!
LUNCHEONS AND TEAS
R.D. LOW Baker and C
WEDNESDAY
TWO TWO AN' NINES, PLEASE!
BLUSH
CRIVVENS! THE TWA AN' NINES!
THURSDAY AT THE PALAIS
GRACIOUS ME! THERE'S DAPHNE WI' HER LAD AGAIN! MY! HE'S NO' BAD LOOKIN'!
FRIDAY
NOW HERE ARE THE VERY SMARTEST NEW ENGAGEMENT RINGS!
OH, I LIKE THIS YIN, WITH THE BIG STONE BETTER THAN THE YIN WITH THREE STONES!
MY!
SATURDAY
THAT'S FIVE NICHTS WE'VE SEEN DAPHNE OOT WI' HER LAD THIS WEEK!
AYE! AN' LAST NICHT I SAW HER AN' HIM CHOOSIN' ENGAGEMENT RINGS!
HE'S TA'EN HER TAE DANCES, TREATED HER TAE HER TEA AN' TAE THE PICTERS AN' A' THING!
HERE'S DAPHNE COMIN' UP THE ROAD NOO!
WHEN SHE COMES IN WE'LL ASK HER A' ABOOT IT!
I WONDER WHEN THE WEDDIN' WILL BE? SHE'LL WANT ME TAE BE A BRIDESMAID!
FANCY OOR DAPHNE GETTIN' MARRIED AFORE MAGGIE! WHA WID HAE THOCHT IT?
HEY! WE'RE NO' TAE BE PAGE BOYS YE KEN AH, NO!
I HEAR HER COMIN' UP THE STAIR!
HOO DID YE NO' BRING YER LAD IN TAE SEE WIS, DAPHNE? LET'S SEE YER ENGAGEMENT RING! - WHEN ARE YE GETTIN' MARRIED? — WHIT'S HIS NAME?
MY LAD? OH, NO! THAT'S MA CHUM'S LAD! I'VE BEEN KEEPIN' HIM COMPANY A' THIS WEEK! YE SEE, BELLA IS ON THE NICHT SHIFT AN' SHE DIDNA' WANT ONY ITHER LASSIE TAE GET HER HOOKS ON HIM. SHE SAID HE WID BE SAFE WI' DAPHNE BROON!
HA! HA! HA!
YOU'RE TELLIN' ME!

in *"Army of One!"*

(Original movie 1993)

THE BROONS® in "Blades of Glory!"

(Original movie 2007)

THE BROONS® in "High Wide and Handsome!"

(Original movie 1937)

in "Homeward Bound!"

(Original movie 1993)

A classic family portrait painted by Dudley Watkins for the cover of the 1941 Broons Book.

THE BROONS

Another wonderful painting by Dudley Watkins. It is wartime and Hen and Joe Broon are at home on leave. This painting went out as a jigsaw instead of an annual book in 1944. Wartime paper shortages meant that DC Thomson were unable to print The Broons book that year.

The same 10 Glebe Street living room today. Some things have stayed the same and yet, everything has changed. Drawn and coloured in 2014 by Steven White and Finn Cramb.

Dudley Watkins evocative Broons at the seaside painting. This too was used as a jigsaw picture in 1946. Again this was due to there being no Broons book that year.

The Broons family at the beach today. The fun picture by Steven White and Finn Cramb 2014.

THE TASTIEST DISH IN A' THE WORLD

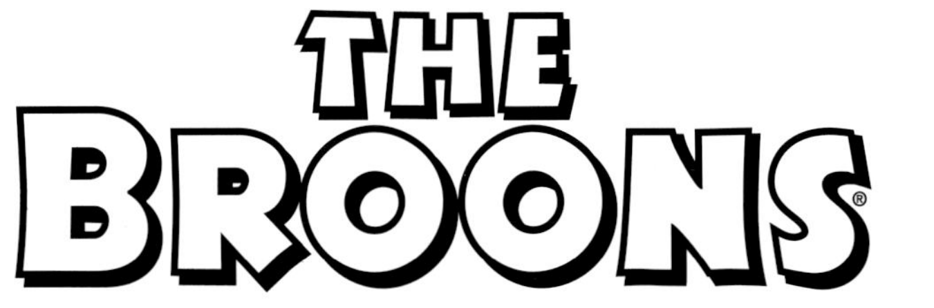

in *"Caravan!"*

(Original movie 1934)

OOR WULLIE
in
"Animal Farm!"
(Original movie 1954)

GONE WALKIES!
I'M TAKIN' HARRY FOR A WALK IN THE COUNTRYSIDE THE DAY
AH! GET A WHIFF O' THAT FRESH AIR, LADS!
YEE-UGH! TOO FRESH AT TIMES, AH'LL TELL YE!
JINGS! WILL YE LOOK AT THE SIZE O' YON BULL.
IF I WAS A SPANISH LADDIE, I'D MAK' A BRAW BULL FIGHTER! EL WULLIE!
C'MON, HARRY. LET'S PLAY AT BULLFIGHTS. I'LL BE THE MATADOR.
OLE, EL HARRY! OLE!
STAMP!
?
C'MON, YOU DAFT DUG! CHARGE MY HANKIE.
ACH, NAW! NO' LIKE THAT!
GRRRR!
GIMME! OOF! WHIT'S THAT?
BUMP!
MOOO!
CRIVVENS! THE BULL!
HELP MA BOAB! RUN FOR IT, HARRY!
BULL? SOME BULL! I'M JIST TAKIN' AULD DAISY THE COO IN FER HER MILKIN'. THAE TOONIES!!
I'M STICKIN' TAE BULL'S-EYES!
KHH.

THE BROONS in "The Music Never Stopped!"
(Original movie 2011)
I FEEL LIKE A BIT O' MUSIC THE DAY.
BRAW IDEA.
ME'S WATERING PLANTS.
I LOVE THIS NEW ANE FRAE "WET WET WET."
I REALLY FANCY THON MARTY PELLOW.
SUDDENLY...
MUSIC? THON'S NO' MUSIC! I'LL GIE YE REAL MUSIC.
AW! STICK IT BACK OAN!
THESE ARE MY MOUNTAINS...
SWAY!
KENNETH McKELLAR ... BRAW STUFF!
BUT THEN...
YOU YOUNG ANE'S HAVE GOT IT A' WRANG! WHIT WE NEED IS LIVE MUSIC!
CLICK!
OCH! NAW! NO' THE PIPES!!
AYE. IT'LL BE A RARE TREAT.
GOT TAE GIE THE PIPES A GUID BLAW TAE KICK START THEM.
DEEP BREATH!
HOWL!
GLUBB!
WHIT OAN...?
THEY'RE A' INTAE "WET WET WET" NOO! MUSIC TAE MY EARS! HEH!
ME'S WATERED YON TARTAN PLANT THIS MORNING.
KEN H. HARRISON.

in *"The Bucket List!"*

(Original movie 2007)

THE BROONS in "The Box!"
(Original movie 2009)
I WANT TAE SEE AMERICAN FITBA'!
THE GARDENING PROGRAMME'S ON B.B.C.!
I'D LIKE TAE SEE THE FILM IF YE DINNA MIND!
JUST LOOK AT THIS! THAT TV CAUSES NOTHIN' BUT ARGUMENTS!
I'LL SETTLE THIS! THERE! THE PLUG'S OOT! NAEBODY GETS TAE WATCH ANYTHIN'!
WE'LL DAE WHAT WE DID AFORE WE HAD TV! WE'LL HAE A FAMILY EVENIN'! LET'S START WI' A GAME O' CARDS! HAVENA PLAYED FOR YEARS!
NO' PLEASED
ACH, GO ON THEN!
NOW, IS THIS NO' BRAW? FINE AN' QUIET!..
SNAP!
IT'S MINE! I GOT TWA KINGS!
AWA' AN BILE YER HEID! IT'S MY SNAP!
ME GOT IT!
MEN!
SNAP? I THOUGHT WE WERE PLAYIN' WHIST!
YOU'RE CHEATIN', YER ARMS ARE OWER LANG!
TWA KINGS! WHAUR? IT'S SPECS YER NEEDIN'!
HEY, WHAUR'S PAW GONE?
HE WIZ HERE A MINUTE AGO!
WID YE BELIEVE IT! EFTER A' HE SAID! NOW HE'S WATCHIN' THE BOX!
OCH, YE CANNA' WIN IN THIS HOOSE! I'M WATCHIN' 'DOCTOR FINLAY'!
KEN. H. HARRISON.

OOR WULLIE
in "Dog Day Afternoon!"
(Original movie 1975)

WULLIE'S ON HIS KNEES AFORE ME. HOW ROMANTIC!
AWA' YE GO, PRIMROSE! CAN YE NO' SEE I'M JUST WATCHIN' HARRY? HE'S LOOKIN' FOR RATS!
THAT IS DISGUSTING!
OCH, THERE ARE THINGS WOMEN DINNA UNDERSTAND!
YOU AN' HARRY HAVE BEEN INVITED TO PRIMROSE'S WEE DOGGY'S BIRTHDAY PARTY.
YER NECK'LL HAE TAE BE SCRUBBED, LADDIE!
HOWL! WHIT ARE YOU SMIRKIN' AT, HARRY?
SCRUB!
YOU'LL HAE TAE GET BRUSHED UP AN' A'! HAH!
JINGS! A BOW COLLAR! POOR DUG!
HOW SWEET!
AT THE PARTY—
WE BROCHT YER DUG A PREZZIE. WHAUR'S THE TRIFLE?
ISN'T THIS EXCITING, PANSY? WULLIE AND HARRY HAVE BROUGHT YOU A PRESENT. HOW NICE OF THEM!
DIG INTAE THE TRIFLE TIME.
FAINT!
SHRIEK! IT'S A DEID RAT!
FAINT!
AYE! A RICHT THUMPER!
BEGONE! AND TAKE THAT REVOLTING OBJECT WITH YOU!
HARRY'S NO' THAT BAD, AN' HOW ABOOT A A DOGGY BAG FULL O' TRIFLE?
ACH! RATS TAE WUMMIN' AN' SAFT DUGS! PITY ABOOT THON TRIFLE THOUGH!
KEN. H HARRISON.

THE BROONS®
in "The Secret Garden!"
(Original movie 1993)

SNORE!
I'M GOING TO WATER MY PLANT. IT'S NOT BEEN LOOKING TOO GOOD!
SORRY, PAW! ME DIDNA MEAN TO WATER YOU!
WHIT?
I'LL FIX UP A FEW WINDAE BOXES! PLANTS SHOULD BE OOTSIDE!
I'M A' SOAKED IN MUDDY WATER! I'LL NEED A BATH!
CRIVVENS! WHIT'S A' THIS?
WE'RE JUST SOAKIN' A' THE HOOSE PLANTS!
I'LL PLANT A FEW SEEDS O' MY AIN IN THE BOX OOTSIDE THE BATHROOM!
NOW FOR A BIT O' PEACE! A NICE RELAXING BATH! I DESERVE A WEE REST NOW I'VE GOT RID O' A' THAE PLANTS!
NO! LOOK AT THIS! A' THAE BIRDS ARE EATIN' MY SEEDS! QUICK-GET THE WINDAE BOXES INSIDE AFORE THE BRUTES RUIN A' MY WORK!
IT'S AMAZIN' HOW FOWK CHANGE THEIR TUNE EFTER PUTTIN' A BIT O' WORK INTO SOMETHING!

OOR WULLIE in "Heatwave!"
(Original movie 1982)
IT'S HOT NOW! ABOOT TIME AN' A'!
A KNOTTED HANKIE'S NAE GUID FOR THE SUN, WULLIE! TRY A BASEBALL CAP!
BASEBALL'S NO' MY IMAGE, BOB!
WHAT ABOOT THIS! GRANDAD WORE IT WHEN HE PLAYED IN GOAL FOR RANGERS.
COOL OR WHAT?
AYE, YER GRANDFAITHER PLAYED IN GOAL FOR CELTIC TAE! ONLY IT WAS STOORIEBURN RANGERS AN' THE SOSHIE CELTIC! BUT ANYWAY . . .
. . . IT'S MY PENTIN' BUNNET NOW! SO YE'LL HAE TAE FIND YER AIN SUN HAT!
AYE, THANKS!
HERE, MAYBE THIS AULD BROLLY WID KEEP THE SUN AFF! A KINDA PARASOL-THINGY . . .
NAE HARM IN TRYIN' IT OOT!
CRIVVENS! IT'S A'HOLES! IT'S NO' SUNBURN I'LL BE GETTIN', IT'LL BE SUNSPOTS!
ACH, THIS IS THE VERY DAB! NAE CHANCE O' US GETTING SUNBURN IN HERE!
HERE'S YER BILL, WULLIE! TWA EXTRA-SPECIAL KNICKERBOCKERS!
SHOCKER!
CORNER CAFE BILL
JINGS! I THOCHT HE WANTED US TAE PAY FOR THE CAFE! NAE SUNBURN — JUST GOT MY FINGERS BURNT WI' THE BILL!
NUTHIN' FOR IT! I'LL JUST HAE TAE USE THE KNOTTED HANKIE TAE KEEP THE SUN AFF!
WULLIE! YOU'VE FORGOTTEN! ADMIT IT! YOU HAVE FORGOTTEN! HOW COULD YOU! YOU . . . YOU . . .
FORGOTTEN? WHA? ME?
THINKING FAST!
WULL'S LASS.
NO! NO! I NEVER FORGET! HOW COULD I EVER FORGET YOUR . . . YOUR . . . YOUR BIRTHDAY!! THAT'S IT! HAPPY BIRTHDAY, PRIMROSE!
HE'S GOT IT!
IMPRESSED!
WELL . . .
AN' LOOK! I TIED FOWER KNOTS IN THIS HANKIE JUST IN CASE I DID FORGET! . . . NO' THAT I DID, MIND!
WULLIE IS COOL!
OH, WULLIE! YOU DID REMEMBER! WHAT HAVE YOU GOT FOR ME!
ER . . . I . . . I DECIDED TAE LEND YE JEEMY FOR THE WHOLE DAY!
HE'S BLOWN IT!!
A MOOSE! SHRIEK!
SQUEAK!
ACH, IT'S THE HEAT! IT FRIES YER BRAIN!
KEN.H. HARRISON.

OOR WULLIE in "Sweet Smell of Success!"

(Original movie 1957)

"Fight Club!"

(Original movie 1999)

THE BROONS
in "The Ghost Train!"
(Original movie 1941)
I HEAR HIM COMIN' NOW!
TRY NO' TAE LAUGH AT THE AULD GOWK!
WHIT ARE YOU LOT LAUGHIN' AT?
HEE-HEE! YER WIG — YE LOOK RIDICULOUS!
HOI! WHIT DID I TELL YE?
IF YE'RE WEARIN' THAT TAE THE FAIR WI' US, WATCH OOT FOR THE FAIRGROUND DOGS — THEY'LL THINK IT'S A CAT ON YER HEID!
TCHAH! YOU JUST DINNA KEN STYLE WHEN YE SEE IT!
AT THE FAIRGROUND
HOOP-LA
GHOST TRAIN
WHAT'LL WE TRY FIRST, BAIRN?
GHOSTIE TRAIN, GRANPAW!
SO
HERE GOES — I HOPE IT'S NO' TOO SCARY!
SOON AFTER
DARTS
MAW! PAW! COME AN' SEE THIS!
WHIT IS IT?
JINGS!
HA-HA! ME DIDNAE LIKE YOU LAUGHIN' AT MY GRANPAW, SO . . .
. . . ME FRIGHTENED HIM INTAE GROWIN' REAL HAIR!
HA-HA! GRANPAW'S HAD A HAIR-RAISIN' EXPERIENCE!
HELP MA BOAB! THAT WAS TOO SCARY!
KEN.H. HARRISON.

in "Short Cuts!"

(Original movie 1993)

"Canoe Man!"

(Original movie 2010)

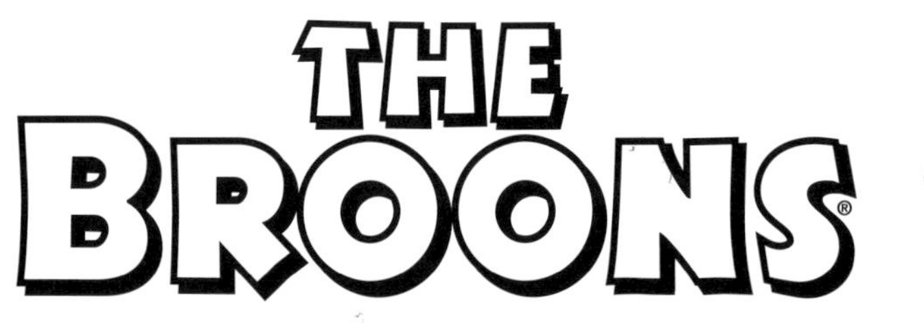

in *"The Fast and the Furious!"*

(Original movie 2001)

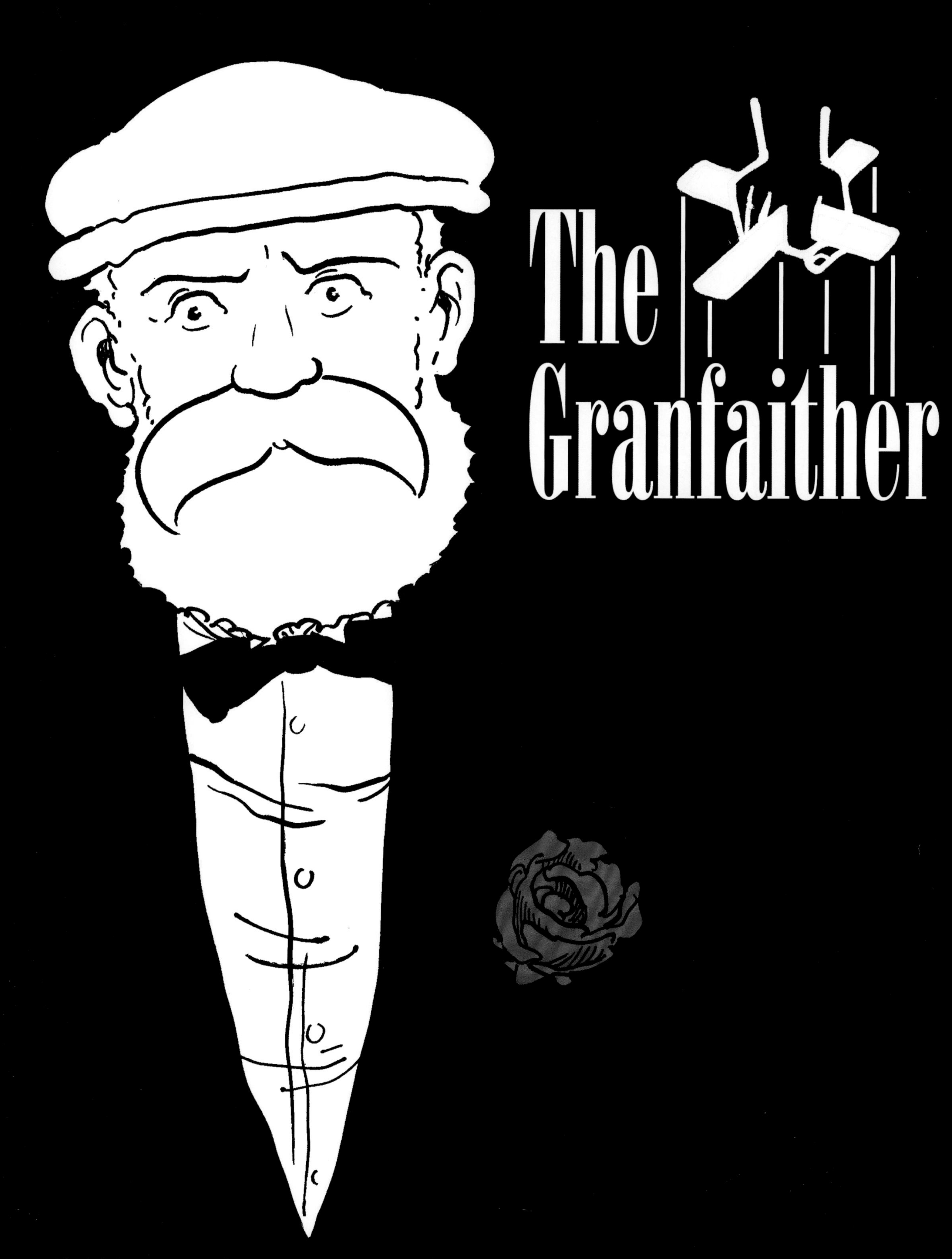

"I'll gie them an offer they cannae refuse."

Granpaw Broon

Another Year Younger

Granpaw Broon was doon in the dumps.

"Ach, I'm getting auld," he moaned to himself. "I've anither birthday coming and it looks like the family's forgotten. Mind you, I canna blame them. I've had that mony. There's been none o' thae wee hints like, "Are you needin' a new bunnet, Granpaw?" or "Wid ye like onything special for yer tea?" or "What size o' shirt dae ye tak, Granpaw?"

" I nearly forgot my birthday masel. It was Jessie Easton at The Legion that reminded me it was comin' up. I can hardly mind what I was doin' yesterday yet I remember when I could play fitba a' day and then hae a round o' golf at night. In fact, I was captain o' the works' team and we played in oor local league. Och, listen to me – an auld manny, richt enough, goin' on aboot the auld days. I'll put some music on an' cheer masel up."

"...an' if ye say it's a braw bricht moonlicht nicht, ye're a'richt, ye ken!"

"Ha, ha! We used tae hae a braw laugh wi' that song in the regiment when we'd ask the Sassenachs tae try tae say the words."

Suddenly, Granpaw's thoughts were interrupted by a loud banging on the door. There on the doorstep stood Maw wi' a face like thunder and The Bairn.

"Will you turn that racket doon?" yelled Maw. "Ye're worse than a teenager! We heard you halfway doon the street. I've been knockin' for ages, ye silly auld fool! Can ye mind The Bairn? I've tae go oot!"

And off she stomped before Granpaw could reply.

The Bairn giggled.

"How can ye be a silly auld fool AND a teenager, Granpaw? Maw's silly!"

Granpaw lifted The Bairn and swung her around.

"Ye're right, ma wee lamb," he laughed. "You always know how to cheer up yer old Granpaw. Now what wid ye like tae dae the day?"

"Me wants tae go tae the park," answered The Bairn.

"Then that's what we'll do," said Granpaw.

On the way to the park, The Bairn began to cry.

"What's wrong, ma wee lamb?" asked Granpaw.

"Me's hungry," sobbed The Bairn. "Me didnae eat ma dinner cos Maw was in a rush."

"Och, " sighed Granpaw, "an' we're no' near a shop or even an ice cream van. Ye'll hae to wait til we get to the park, lass."

The Bairn howled even louder. Then Granpaw's sharp eye sighted a rosy red apple on a tree.

"Hmm, " he wondered, and he had a quick look round. "Nae polis in sight."

Without another thought, Granpaw shimmied up the tree and plucked the rosy apple. Then he slid down and gave it to The Bairn.

"For the apple of my eye," he grinned.

"Aww, Granpaw," smiled The Bairn. "You're the best!"

And she gave him a big hug.

The Bairn had finished her apple by the time they reached the park but she and Granpaw shared a picnic of crisps and biscuits followed by ice cream and juice from the park van.

"That was yummy, Granpaw, " said The Bairn. "Me wants to play skipping now".

"You skip and I'll watch you," tried Granpaw, but The Bairn wasn't having that.

"No, you skip too, Granpaw, " insisted The Bairn.

"But we need someone else to hold an end of the rope, " reasoned Granpaw.

"Naw, we can tie it to this pole," answered The Bairn. "Look!"

"I'll caw the handle and you jump," instructed The Bairn.

"Okay, " chuckled Granpaw, "but I think the ice cream in my tummy might turn into a milk shake!"

Granpaw soon persuaded The Bairn to take a turn at jumping and, after half an hour or so, she grew tired. They were just about to head home when The Bairn spotted a pretty butterfly.

"Oh, look, Granpaw! Pretty butterfly! Me needs one for nursery class! Catch it, please!"

Luckily, a discarded fishing net lay by the duck pond and Granpaw scooped it up and set off in pursuit of the butterfly.

"Anything for you, mah wee lamb.

I'll do my best, " puffed Granpaw. "If you need a butterfly for nursery, then you'll have one."

Granpaw gently caught the butterfly in the net then he and The Bairn found an empty drinks carton with a lid. The Bairn held the butterfly in the net with her hand over the top to prevent the insect from escaping while Granpaw pierced air holes into the lid of the carton. Next they transferred the butterfly to the carton, popped on the lid and prepared for home.

Just as they were leaving the park, The Bairn saw her brothers' pal, Ryan Younger, with a skateboard under his arm and a face like fizz.

"What's wrong, Ryan?" asked The Bairn.

"This skateboard's rubbish," moaned Ryan. "It won't go."

"Let me have a look at it, " suggested Granpaw.

The boy gave Granpaw the skateboard and soon the old man saw the problem.

"A wheel's squint," he said. "I'll soon sort that," and he knocked it back into shape.

"Now I'd better just check it out for you," he offered, and he whizzed off on the board.

"Yay!" cried The Bairn. " My Granpaw's the bestest ever!"

"Yeah," agreed Ryan as Granpaw returned the skateboard to him. "Thanks, Mr Broon. You're a good boarder too! I'm impressed."

Granpaw laughed and said, "Glad to help."

When Granpaw and The Bairn got home, Maw was waiting for them.

"Where have you been? You're late for tea," she said, annoyed.

"We had great fun at the park," answered The Bairn. "My Granpaw's the best!"

"Did your Granpaw remember he's playing his bagpipes at the Legion tonight for Jim George's birthday?" asked Maw. "He'd better have some puff left."

"Whit! Nobody told me!" said Granpaw, shocked.

"Oh, aye we did," replied Maw. "You'd better eat yer tea and smarten yersel up quick!"

Granpaw made it to the Legion by the skin o' his teeth. No one was around.

"They must a' be inside," he thought so he puffed and he blew and he tuned up his pipes then he marched into the hall proudly playing "Scotland the Brave"!

There was a great cheer and everyone applauded then Granpaw noticed his whole family – even The Bairn – there!

"What the....?" began Granpaw and then he saw a banner saying, "Surprise! Happy Birthday, Granpaw Broon!"

"And you didnae tell me," he gasped.

"It was a secret," she chuckled. "Have you got plenty puff left to blow out your candles now, Granpaw?"

"Let's find out," laughed Granpaw. "One, two, three..."

Granpaw put down his pipes.

"You mean... this party's for me?" he asked shakily.

"Yes," laughed Maw. "That's why I needed The Bairn to take you out this afternoon - so I could get everything ready!"

Granpaw looked at The Bairn.

"Hooray!" cheered everyone. "Happy Birthday to the best Granpaw in the world!"

Granpaw went home singing and dancing and thanking the best family world!

HAME ALONe

A FAIMILY COMEDY WITHOOT THE FAIMILY

In 1992 an enormous change occurs within the pages of the Sunday Post newspaper, home of The Broons and Oor Wullie. The two classic strips which had always been printed in black and white appear in colour.

It is not full colour, the characters and speech bubbles remain in black and white. This gives the strips a strange washed out look and it is not popular with the readers. Many of the readers had been following the strips since their introduction in 1936 and did not take kindly to change.

The experiment runs for two years but Broons and Oor Wullie fans continue to complain about it being better in black and white. They get their wish in August 1994. Peace returns to Glebe Street once again.

A fine series of Broons and Oor Wullie art, coloured for your enjoyment.

OOR WULLIE
ICING SUGAR
STRAWBERRY JAM
RAISINS
DUDLEY D. WATKINS

THE BROONS
EXIT
EXIT
DUDLEY D. WATKINS

OOR WULLIE
DUDLEY D WATKINS
Wullie's Ma kens what to do—
A leather patch'll no' wear through!

THE BROONS
DUDLEY D. WATKINS

THERE'S NAE PLAN AT 'A!

in *"Man in the Chair!"*

(Original movie 2007)

in *"Just the Ticket!"*

(Original movie 1999)

in "Primal Fear!"

(Original movie 1996)

THE BROONS in "Loch Ness!"
(Original movie 1996)
HAE YE GOT SPOOLS IN YER CAMERAS, YOU TWA? —BECAUSE WE'LL MAYBE SEE THE LOCH NESS MONSTER!
AYE! WE MICHT!
SEEVEN GROWN UPS AN' FOWER JUVENILES!
WHIT IS IT, A FITBA' TEAM?
WATTIE'S TOURS GLENCOE AND LOCH NESS
IN GLENCOE
JINGS! ISN'T THAT A BONNY SICHT?
OH, WHIT RARE!
I JUIST FEEL I COULD SIT DOON AN' WRITE POETRY!
WID YE LIKE A CHEW, LAD?
AT LOCH NESS
WE'RE STOPPIN' FOR THE VIEW OF LOCH NESS!
HEY!—LOOK! THERE'S SOMETHING SWIMMING OOT THERE!—GET YER CAMERAS, MAYBE IT'S THE MONSTER!
I'D BETTER TAK A FEW QUICK ANES.
QUICK!—TAK IT NOO, HORACE! IT'S COMIN' UP OOT'N THE WATTER!
IT'S GOT RED, WHITE AN' BLUE SPOTS ON IT!
IT IS!—I CAN SEE IT WINKIN' AT ME!
IT'S NO THE MONSTER AT A'—IT'S A TREE TRUNK!
GIE ME THEY GLASSES!
WEEL, THAT'S THE LOT—MA SPOOL'S FINISHED!
COME OOT O' THERE, GRAN'PAW! FANCY, YE'VE GOT YERSEL' A' WEET!
WHIT'S GRAN'PAW DAEIN' WADIN' IN THE WATTER?
HEY, GRAN'PAW! THE LOCH NESS MONSTER'LL GET YE IF YE DON'T WATCH OUT!!
COMIN' HAME IN THE CHARRY
YE KEN, I DIDNA SEE THE MONSTER VERY WEEL, BUT MA CAMERA WILL SHOW IT UP!
WEEL, I THINK I SAW IT! IT LOOKED A' TARTAN TAE ME!
SHIVER
ARE YE WARM IN THE RUG GRAN'PAW? YER CLAES'LL SUNE DRY, HANGIN' UP!
IT HAD FOUR HUMPS AN' TWA HEIDS!
NA! I TELL YE IT HAD SPIKES STICKIN' OOT O' IT'S BACK, AN' A HEID AT EACH END!
WEEL, WE'LL SEE WHIT IT WIS LIKE WHEN THE FILM'S DEVELOPED!
NEXT DAY
HERE'S THE SNAPS FROM THE CHEMIST'S!

THE BROONS in "Picnic!"

(Original movie 1955)

OOR WULLIE® in "The Great Outdoors!"
(Original movie 1988)
LET'S GO CAMPIN'-OOT AT BERRY HILL!
GOODOH! I'LL DAE A' THE WOOD CHOPPIN'.
I'LL DAE A' THE WASHIN' UP, AN' YOU DAE THE COOKIN', WULLIE!
ON THE WAY
I'M BUSY LOOKIN' FOR WID TAE CHOP.
I'D HELP YE TAE HAUL THE CART, WULLIE, BUT WASHIN' UP IS MY JOB.
HUH! EXCUSES FOR NO' HELPIN' TAE PULL THIS HEAVY PILER!
AT BERRY HILL
I'M AWAY FOR WOOD.
ARE YE NO' TAE HELP ME PIT UP THE TENT?
MY JOB'S WASHIN' DISHES. I DINNA BOTHER ABOOT TENTS.
WELL, IT'S YOUR JOB TAE DAE THE COOKIN'. SO WE'LL AWA' FOR A STROLL. SEE AN' HAE THE DENNER READY WHEN WE GET BACK.
JINGS! I'M AYE WORKIN' IN THIS CAMP!
I'LL MAK' STEW WI' CORNED BEEF AND AN AULD NEEP. IT SMELLS FUNNY!
I'LL SEE IF IT TASTES BETTER~GROOGH~TERRIBLE!
I'VE JUST MINDED! IT'S STOVIES FOR DENNER AT HAME THE DAY. IF I HURRY, I'LL JUST BE IN TIME.
AT HOME
I THOCHT YOU WERE CAMPIN'?
AYE! BUT THE COOKIN'S NO' VERY GOOD.
I'LL USE MY BIKE, AN' HURRY BACK AFORE BOB AN' SOAPY COME FOR THEIR DENNER.
I DINNA WANT THEM TAE KEN I'VE BEEN HAME FOR MY DENNER, SO I'LL HIDE THE BIKE HERE.
DINNER TIME
GAW! THIS TASTES TERRIBLE!
ARE YOU NO' HAEIN' ONY?
ME?~ER~NO, I'VE HAD MINE.
NEXT MORNING
OH, WELL, I SUPPOSE I'LL NEED TAE GET UP FIRST AN' MAK' THE BREAKFAST.
ACH! THAT'S THE BREAKFAST RUINED. THAT EGG'S GOT AN AWFY SMELL! I WONDER WHIT MA'S COOKIN' FOR BREAKFAST AT HAME?
I'LL NIP HAME AN' SEE, AN' BE BACK AFORE THEY WAKEN UP.
HOME AGAIN
SO YE'VE COME HAME FOR YER BREAKFAST!
AYE! I GOT A BAD EGG IN THE PAN. BOB AN' SOAPY ARE STILL SLEEPIN'.
THAE TWA WILL NEVER KEN I'VE BEEN HAME.
I SEE THEY'RE NO' UP YET. I'LL HIDE THE BIKE AMONG THE WHINS AGAIN.
JINGS! WULLIE, YE'RE AN AWFY COOK~THIS BREAKFAST IS TERRIBLE! HOW ARE YOU NO' EATIN' ONY?
I'VE~ER~I'VE HAD MINE.
HI, WULLIE!
LOOK, WULLIE! YE DRAPPIT YER MUDGUARD AFF YER BIKE WHEN YE LEFT THE HOOSE AFTER YER BREAKFAST THIS MORNIN'.
SO YE WENT HAME FOR YER BREAKFAST!
WHAUR'S THE BIKE? HE'S GOT IT HIDDEN!
I'LL USE YOUR BIKE~WE'RE AWA' HAME FOR A DECENT FEED~WE'RE THROUGH WI' CAMPIN'!
AYE! AN' YE CAN CARRY A' THE STUFF BACK. I'M GOIN' HAME ON MY CART~I'M STARVIN'!
DINNA SPEAK TAE ME ABOOT CAMPIN'!
DUDLEY D. WATKINS

THE BROONS® in "The Weather Man!"

(Original movie 2005)

OOR WULLIE
in "Happy Campers!"
(Original movie 2001)
RIGHT, THEN, WULLIE ~ YOU GIVE ME A HAND WI' THE GARDEN AN' I'LL GIVE YOU MY AULD BELL TENT. I'M AWA' OOT NOW, BUT JUIST YOU WEED THE LETTUCES, WATER A' THE VEGETABLES, WASH THE GREENHOOSE WINDIES, AN' TIDY UP THE GARDEN.
O.K., MISTER BAXTER!
I'M GETTIN' A BELL TENT ~ AN' I'LL LET YOU LADS HAE A SHARE IN IT. A' YE NEED TAE DAE IS A WEE BIT O' GAIRDENIN. OF COURSE, I COULD DAE IT MASEL', BUT JUIST OOT O' KINDNESS, I'M LETTIN' YOU LADS IN ON IT.
OH, WULLIE, THAT'S AWFY GOOD O' YE!
YE'RE A REAL PAL!
WE'LL GET TO WORK NOW. YOU WEED THE LETTUCES, SOAPY, AN' YOU WATER THE VEGETABLES, BOB.
O.K., WULLIE!
YE'RE DOIN' FINE, SOAPY, BUT YE'VE MISSED A WEED OR TWA HERE!
YE'RE GETTIN' FELL BOSSY LIKE, AREN'T YE?
ARE YE ~PECH~ NO' DOIN' ONY WORK YERSEL', WULLIE?
OH, AYE! I'LL BE DOIN' THE JOBS THAT NEED SKILL AN' BRAINS.
LOOK! WULLIE'S USIN' HIS SKILL AN' BRAINS TAE WASH THE GREENHOOSE WINDIES!
HUH! HE'S MAKIN' A SCARECRAW NOW!
ACH! IT'S A BIT SAFT-LOOKIN' YET.
AH! THAT'S BETTER ~ NOW, YOU LADS, GET ON WI' THE BURYIN' O' THE RUBBISH.
HOW CAN YE NO' GIE US A HAND WI' THE HEAVY JOBS?
GOOD! HERE'S THE ~PANT~ BELL TENT AT LAST ~PECH~
HERE'S YER TENT, WULLIE. YE'VE DONE A GRAND JOB!
IT'S BEEN HARD WORK, BUT IT WIS WORTH IT.
JINGS, THIS TENT'S HEAVY! WHIT ABOOT GOIN' CAMPIN' TAE KINGOODIE KNOWES THIS AFTERNOON?
AYE, WE'LL DAE THAT. I'D HELP YE TAE CARRY THE TENT ~ BUT MY HANDS ARE FULL.
HEY! WHIT ABOOT HAVIN' A LOOK AT THE TENT TAE SEE IF IT'S A' RICHT?
MICHTY ME! IT'S FU' O' HOLES!
HUH! WE'D BE AS WELL CAMPIN' UNDER A FISHIN' NET. YE CAN KEEP YER AULD TENT.
HEY! HELP ME TAE GET THIS AFF THE TRAM-LINES.
AWA' AN' DAE IT YERSEL'.
CRIVVENS! THE TRAM'S RUN OWER THE TENT AN' CUT IT INTAE THREE BITS!
THAT AFTERNOON
IT'S BRAW OOT HERE ON KINGOODIE KNOWES THE DAY ~ AN' TAE THINK WE MICHT HAE BEEN CAMPIN' HERE.
LOOK, SOME LUCKY LAD'S GOT A TENT PITCHED JUIST WHERE WE WOULD HAE BEEN.
MICHTY ME! IT'S WULLIE ~ B-BUT THE BELL TENT'S GOT AWFY WEE.
AYE! YON TRAM CAR CUT IT INTAE THREE BITS ~ AN' THE TOP BIT DISNAE HAE ONY HOLES IN IT!
JINGS! HE'S DONE US AGAIN!
SNORE
DUDLEY D. WATKINS

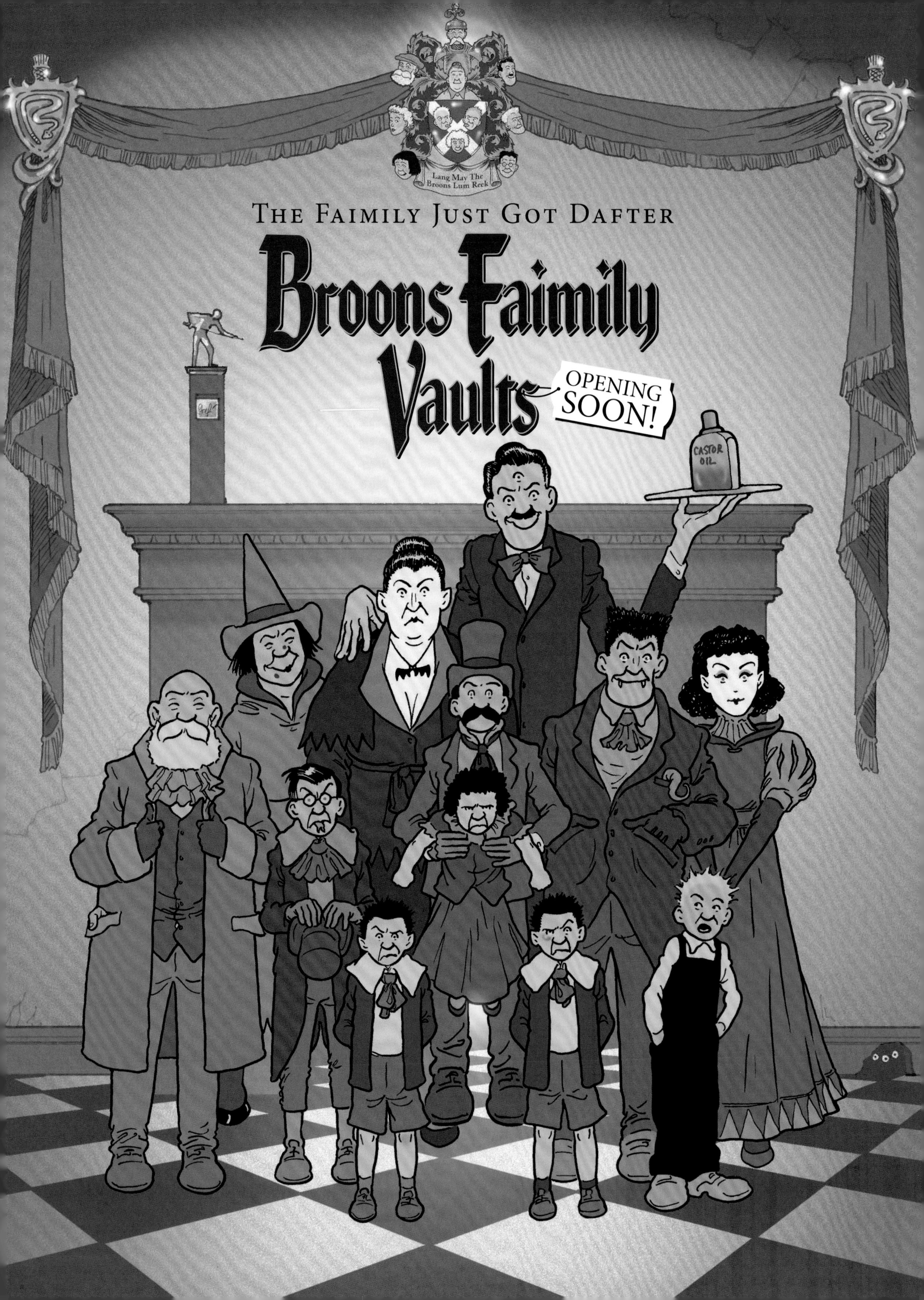

Lang May The Broons Lum Reek
THE FAIMILY JUST GOT DAFTER
Broons Faimily Vaults
OPENING SOON!
CASTOR OIL

PAW'S

IT'S SAFE WHILE THEY'RE IN THE WATER

"Some Like it Hot!"

(Original movie 1959)

in "The Climb!"

(Original movie 1997)

OOR WULLIE

in "Deluge!"
(Original movie 1933)

IS THERE GONNAE BE A SUMMER THIS YEAR?
I'LL DAE A QUICK HUNDRED METRE DASH TAE GET TAE THE SHED . . .
INSIDE —
NO' MUCH O' A DAY FOR A GANG MEETIN', EH?
YOU SAID IT!
WHAT'LL WE DAE THE' DAY? IT'S POORIN' OOTSIDE!
JINGS! WE COULD FIX THE 'GANG HUT' ROOF, MAYBE!
GUID IDEA!
PLOP!
THERE'LL BE STUFF IN HERE WE CAN FIX IT WI' — FROM INSIDE!
AYE — NO WAY AM I GOIN' ON THE ROOF IN THAT RAIN!
IF I MOVE A' THIS JUNK, THERE MICHT BE SOMETHIN' DOON HERE FOR PATCHIN' UP THE ROOF.
PULLIN' HARD!
BUT —
THUD!
AW, NO!
PLOP!
OCH! MAIR HOLES!
TUG!
LOOK! IF I DAE THIS, THE BROLLY CATCHES THE RAIN! BRILLIANT OR WHIT?
SO, SOON —
OH-OH! THAT BROLLY'S FILLIN' UP NICELY . . .
THAT WAS A BIG FIB, BOB, BUT I CAN TELL A BIGGER AIN . . .
FLIP!
SPLOOSH!
. . . NEVER SHOULD'VE LISTENED TAE YOU . . .
EEJIT!
BUT . . . BUT . . . I WAS TRYIN' MY BEST! . . .
ATCHOO!
KEN. H. HARRISON.

in *"Vertical Limit!"*

(Original movie 2000)

OOR WULLIE
in
"State of Play!"
(Original movie 2009)

FAR AWA'
A' BODY'S AWA' ON HOLIDAY AN' THERE'S NAEBODY TAE PLAY WI'! OCH!
NAW. I DINNA MEAN YOU, HARRY, I MEAN A FRIEND!
WUFF!
WANT TAE PLAY WI' ME?
OH, AYE....
SULK
PRIMROSE! OCH! BUT......
YES?
MICHT AS WELL TEACH YOU A BIT O' FITBA'. SEE IF YE CAN GET THE BALL PAST ME INTAE THE GOAL.
BENDING FREE KICKS LIKE THIS YE MEAN? I CALL THIS ONE MY DAVIE COOPER SPECIAL!
SLAM!
WHAM!
HELP MAH BOAB!
ER.... LET'S TRY ANITHER GAME... ER....
YES..?
SUDJERS! THAT'S IT! TRY AN' DISARM ME IF YE CAN! HAH!
I CAN BE MOST DISARMING, WULLIE! Hiiii!
OOF!
DO YOU SURRENDER?
AYE! AYE! JUST GET AFF!
LET'S PLAY ONE O' MY GAMES NOW!
ACH! WHAT'LL IT BE? MUD WRESTLING?
JUST AS WEEL MY PALS ARE ON HOLIDAY! RIGHT NOO I WANT NAEBODY TAE SEE ME!
MAN'S BEST FRIEND RIGHT ENOUGH.
KEN H. HARRISON

OOR WULLIE® in "Good Will Hunting!"
(Original movie 1997)

COME TO BONNIE LOCH NESS AND SEE THE MONSTER
JINGS! I WONDER IF THERE'S A MONSTER IN SWANNIE PONDS?
I'M OFF MONSTER HUNTIN', ECK.
COUNT ME OOT, WULLIE!
THIS PIE WILL BRING THE MONSTER LEAPIN' OOT.
MICHTY! IT'S THE M....MONSTER!
ACH! YE'RE NO' FUNNY, ECK!
THAT FAIRLY GOT HIM GOIN'!
MONSTERS ARE BALONEY! AH'M NO WASTIN' A GOOD PIE!
MUNCH!
I JUST SAW NESSIE DOON AT SWANNIE PONDS.
WHIT?
COME AWA'IN AND HAE A CUP O' TEA, NESSIE!
OH!
GOOD OLD AUNTIE NESSIE! SHE BROUGHT ME THIS MONSTER STICK O' ROCK!
KHH

GRANPAW BROON
IT'S NO' FINE GETTIN' AULD.

LUMBAGO

THE BROONS in "The Onion Field!"
(Original movie 1979)
DOWN AT GRANPAW'S ALLOTMENT–
ME HELP GRANPAW.
GUID LASS.
AH'LL WIN THE PRIZE FOR THE BIGGEST ONIONS AT THE FLOOER SHOW.
SPECIAL BREW
YOU AYE BEAT TATTIE TAMSON.
YOU'VE GOT TAE BE REAL NICE TAE THEM.
GRANPAW'S SINGIN' TAE AN INGIN!
AYE, YE'LL BE IN TEARS AGAIN, TATTIE TAMSON, WHEN I BEAT THAE PUNY ONIONS O' YOURS.
WE'LL SEE, BROON! SNIFF!
LATER–
10
MAW'S INVITED ME UP FOR A BITE TAE EAT.
EAT UP, GRANPAW. IT'S YOUR FAVOURITE-STEAK AN' ONIONS!
BRAW!
THE BAIRN BROUGHT YOUR INGINS UP FAE THE PLOT, GRANPAW.
WHIT? DINNA TELL ME AH'VE JUST MUNCHED MAH PRIZE ONIONS!!
ME THOUGHT THE ONIONS WOULD LIKE TAE LISTEN TO ONE O' GRANPAW'S OLD HARRY LAUDER RECORDS.
.....MARY MA SCOTS BLUEBELL....
KHH.
THE FLOWER SHOW–
WHIT'S YER SECRET, BROON?
YE'LL HAVE TAE ASK HARRY LAUDER!
WINK
WINK!
3RD
1ST

THE BROONS
in "Cabbage Patch Kids!"
(Original movie 1984)

OCH! THAE CATERPILLARS'LL HAE MY CABBAGE-PATCH EATEN AWA' TAE NOTHING BEFORE LONG!
THEN
WHIT'S UP, GRANPAW?
CATERPILLARS — EATIN' A' MY CABBAGES!
WE'LL COLLECT THEM FOR YE — AT FIVE PENCE A CATERPILLAR!
HM! OKAY! THERE'S NO' THAT MANY O' THE WEE BLIGHTERS!
AWAY IN AN' HAE A CUP O' TEA, GRANPAW — WE'LL SEE YE SHORTLY!
RIGHTO!
SOON AFTER —
KNOCK! KNOCK!
THERE'S EASILY MORE THAN A HUNDRED HERE, GRANPAW — BUT WE'LL SETTLE FOR A FIVER!
JINGS! YE'VE BEEN WORKING HARD! A FIVER . . . ER . . . I'LL JUST GET IT!
HAVE THE BAIRNS GOT SOME KIND O' NATURE PROJECT ON AT SCHOOL, BROON?
I DINNA KEN — WHY DO YE ASK?
IT'S JIST THAT THEY ASKED IF THEY COULD COLLECT THE CATERPILLARS AFF MY PATCH — AN' MISTER MILDEW'S, TWA DOORS DOON!
WHIT?
COME BACK HERE, YE WEE SWINDLERS!
JINGS! THE BAIRNS MUST'VE BEEN BUGGIN' GRANPAW SOMETHING AWFY!
KEN.H. HARRISON.

THE BROONS in "Elephant!"
(Original movie 2003)
DO COME IN!
SIT UP, YOU TWA! THE MINISTER'S HERE ABOOT THE CHURCH FETE.
SNARZZ!
GLOWER!
A FETE WORSE THAN DEATH! HA! HA!
HOW ARE YOU, MRS BROON?
NOW, LADIES, I'LL TELL YOU WHICH STALLS I'D LIKE YOU TO LOOK AFTER....
MRS BROON, A WONDERFUL COOK, WILL BE ON THE HOME BAKERY STALL.
TOO KIND.
MAGGIE, A FINE SEAMSTRESS, ON THE SECOND-HAND CLOTHES AND EMBROIDERY.
TA!
AND DAPHNE... THE WHITE ELEPHANT STALL.
HUMPH!
WHITE ELEPHANT? COO!
NOW, NOW, MY WEE LAMB- WHIT ARE YE GREETIN' ABOOT?
BOOKS
SNIFF!
DAPHNE WILL NO' SELL ME HER WHITE ELEPHANT! ME WANTS IT FOR A PET!
ACH! I TRIED TELLIN' HER I DINNA HAE ONY ELEPHANTS- JUST JUNK!
NEVER YOU MIND, LASS. YOU CAN HAVE MY PINK ELEPHANT I WON ON THE TOMBOLA! CHUCKLE!
HEH!
OH, BRAW! ME CALL HIM EFFIE!
KEN. H. HARRISON.

in *"The Bone Collector!"*

(Original movie 1999)

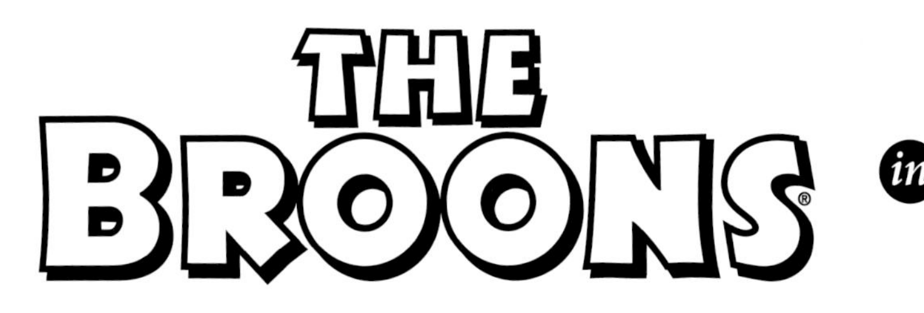

in "Cold Comfort Farm!"

(Original movie 1995)

THE DEPUTIES

FAT BOB, SOAPY SOUTAR AND WEE ECK

in *“Wild, Wild West!”*

(Original movie 1999)

Wee Harry

Oor Wullie's Wise Westie

Wee Harry
Oor Wullie's Wise Westie
OOR WULLIE
HERE'S A LEAD FOR HARRY! IT'S EVEN GOT A "RECALL" BUTTON
BETTER PRESS THE "RECALL" BUTTON.
JOING!
HM! THAT "RECALL" SPRING'S A BIT ON THE STRONG SIDE.
JINGS!
THAT'S THE BIGGEST WEST HIGHLAND TERRIER I EVER SAW!
BOUNCE!
SO I SAYS TAE HIM AND HE SAYS TAE ME!
YE'VE NO' MUCH TAE SAY FOR YERSELF!
NAE WONDER! YOU'RE TALKIN' TAE THE WRONG END!
I HOPE YE DON'T FEED YOUR MUTT UNDER THE TABLE!
NAE! HARRY LIKES TAE FEED ON THE TABLE!
GOBBLE!

Wee Harry
Oor Wullie's Wise Westie

OOR WULLIE

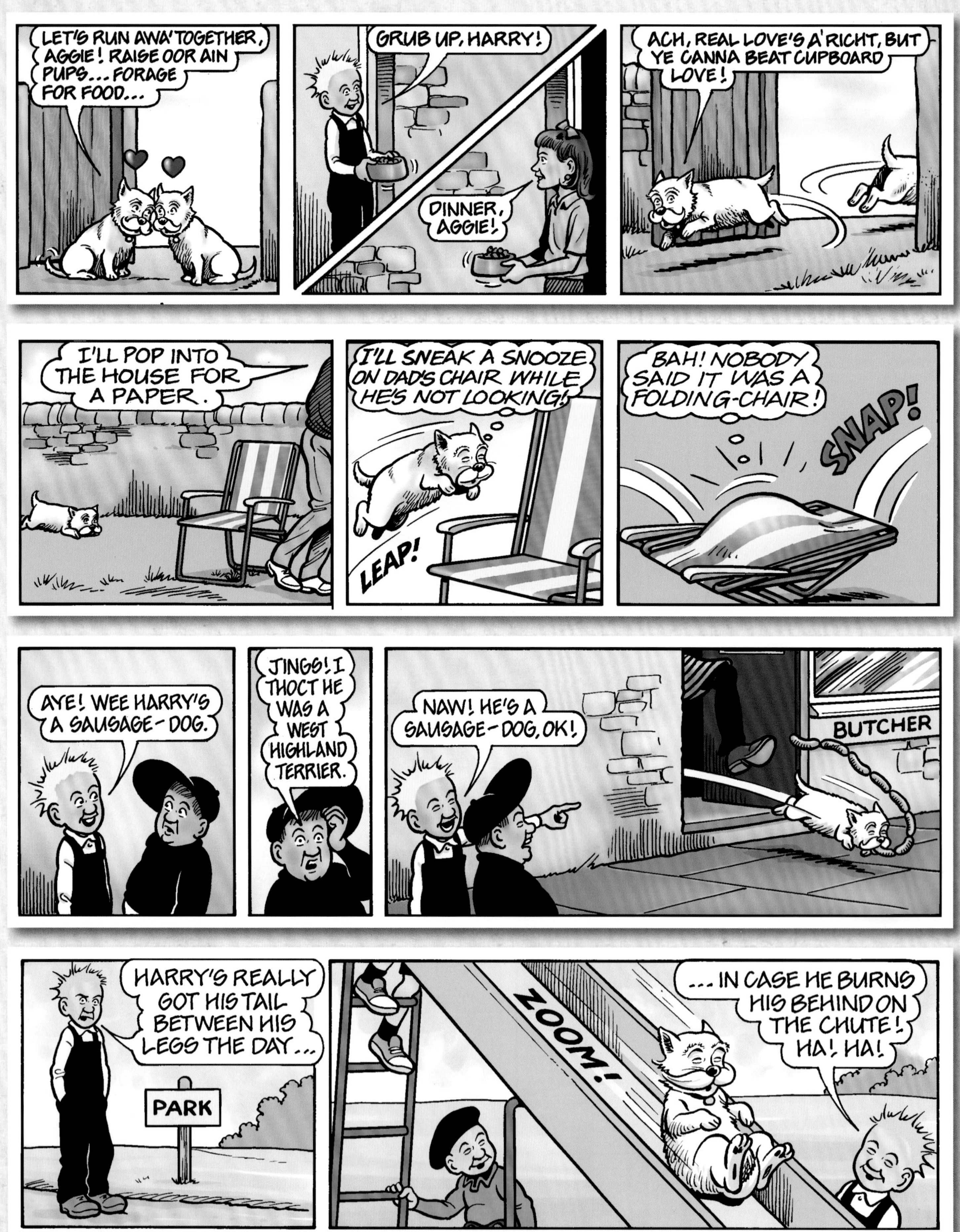
LET'S RUN AWA' TOGETHER, AGGIE! RAISE OOR AIN PUPS... FORAGE FOR FOOD...
GRUB UP, HARRY!
DINNER, AGGIE!
ACH, REAL LOVE'S A'RICHT, BUT YE CANNA BEAT CUPBOARD LOVE!
I'LL POP INTO THE HOUSE FOR A PAPER.
I'LL SNEAK A SNOOZE ON DAD'S CHAIR WHILE HE'S NOT LOOKING!
LEAP!
BAH! NOBODY SAID IT WAS A FOLDING-CHAIR!
SNAP!
AYE! WEE HARRY'S A SAUSAGE-DOG.
JINGS! I THOCT HE WAS A WEST HIGHLAND TERRIER.
NAW! HE'S A SAUSAGE-DOG, OK!
BUTCHER
HARRY'S REALLY GOT HIS TAIL BETWEEN HIS LEGS THE DAY...
PARK
ZOOM!
...IN CASE HE BURNS HIS BEHIND ON THE CHUTE! HA! HA!

Wee Harry
Oor Wullie's Wise Westie

OOR WULLIE

PARK
NO DOGS ALLOWED EXCEPT ON LEAD
NO DOGS ALLOWED EXCEPT ON LEAD
ZOOM!
NAE DOUBT ABOOT IT! YE CAN AYE TELL WHEN HARRY'S IN THE HUFF!
THIS IS GOOD FUN.
IT'S NOT SO EASY IF YOU'RE A SAUSAGE DOG.
WOOF!
WOOF!
WOOF!
GET LOST, HARRY!
ACH! THE CHEEK O' THE BOY... USING MY BONES AS BAILS!

Star of Stage

The wee rascals that are Oor Wullie and his pals haven't made it to Hollywood yet but in 1979 a musical comedy starring Wullie and his pals toured Scotland.

IS THAT OOR WULLIE SINGING?

Seen here in the photograph are Wullie, Soapy Soutar, Fat Bob and Wee Eck. The programme for the show included some Dudley Watkins drawings

MAYBE IT'S HIS CARTIE WHEEL SQUEAKING?
NAW, IT'S HIS PET CRAW.
OVERGROUND THEATRE COMPANY
PRESENTS
OOR WULLIE
A MUSICAL COMEDY FOR ALL THE FAMILY
ON THE FAMOUS CARTOON CHARACTER IN THE SUNDAY POST. PERFORMED UNDER LICENCE FROM D.C. THOMSON'S

OOR WULLIE® In the charts!

2013 Oor Wullie and his Bucket Band playing a version of the Bay City Rollers hit 'Shang-a-Lang' make it into the download charts. The music was produced by ex-Roller Stuart 'Woody' Wood. A film clip accompanied the music and Oor Wullie appeared in the flesh in the guise of lookalike Jamie Webster. Jamie played the authentic Oor Wullie auld zinc bucket.

The animation drawings were added to the live action and the music track. Stuart Wood was pleased with the fact that artist Steve White had taken many years off him and drawn him as he was in 1976. Jamie's Gran made him a pair of tartan trimmed Bay City Roller dungarees especially for the filming.

ONLY MAW BROON COULD TELL HER LADDIES APART

(THE ITHER TWIN HAS GINGER HAIR)

SEVEN BRIDIES
FOR SEVEN BROONS
FORFAR'S FAVOURITE MOVIE

OOR WULLIE®
in "The Big Fisherman!"
(Original movie 1959)

ZZZZ!
C'MON, WULLIE. YE PROMISED TO GO DIGGIN' FER BAIT WI' ME DOON THE BEACH THIS MORNING.
ZZZ! GET LOST, WEE ECK.
JAB!
JINGS! I'M MOVIN'! I'M MOVIN'!
THIS IS WELL PAST THE JOKE.
ZZZZ!
MIND, WULLIE, IT'S THE EARLY BIRD THAT CATCHES THE WORM OR DIGS THEM IN OOR CASE.
SOON HAE PLENTY O' BAIT AT THIS RATE.
BRAW, ECK. ZZZ!
HERE'S A CRAB FOR YER BUCKET, WULLIE. THEY MAK' BRAW BAIT.
AYE, WHITEVER YE SAY.
IN YE GO. NOW TAE GET MAIR SHUT-EYE.
STUFF!
NIP!
YEOW!
WATCH OOT, MAN!
GLUB!
HOWL! GET AFF!
OCH! THERE GOES ALL MY HARD-DUG WORMS.
BAH! YE'RE HOPELESS, MAN! MICHT AS WELL GIE UP.
I'LL GET THE MILK IN THEN TAK' OOT MAH CURLERS.
NAE FISHIN' THE DAY THEN...
HOLD IT, ECK. MA'S CURLERS HAVE JIST GIVEN ME A BRAW IDEA.
MA'S BENDY CURLERS MAK' BRAW "WORMS".
AYE! THEY EVEN WORK TAE!
WHERE'S MY CURLERS?
MUM'S THE WORD! I'LL SNEAK HER CURLERS BACK IN LATER! HEH!
WINK!
KEN.H. HARRISON.

OOR WULLIE
in "Dirty Harry!"
(Original movie 1971)
BUT IT'S POURIN' DOON OUTSIDE!
YOU'RE THE ANE THAT WANTED A DOG, IT NEEDS EXERCISED!
HURRY UP NOW! I'M NO' STANDIN' OOT IN THIS A' DAY!
I HOPE YOU'VE SEEN THE SIGN, WULLIE!
OCH, HE'S JUST... ER... LOOKIN' FOR HIS BONE!
DOG OWNERS! IT IS AN OFFENCE TO ALLOW DOGS TO FOUL THE FOOTPATH
YE'LL HAE T' GO T' THE DOG EXERCISE AREA IN THE PARK!
HERE, THAT'S JUST WHIT I NEED!
PET IGLOO
EXTENDING DOG LEAD
RIGHT, LAD! LET'S GO!
CAT
NOW I CAN BIDE HERE FINE AN' DRY WHILE HARRY SNIFFS ABOUT!
TIME T' REEL HIM IN NOW! IT'S LIKE FISHIN'!
TUG!
WHAT'S HAPPENED? HE'S STUCK!
TUG! TUG!
JINGS! HE'S TANGLED UP WI' ANOTHER DOG ON AN EXTENDIN' LEAD!
THIS IS A RIGHT SCUNNER!
NOW, HAME AFORE I GET SOAKED!
NO!
STAND STILL! I'LL SOON DRY YE AFF!
DROOKIT!
NO' AGAIN!
AN' NOW I HAVE T' GET A BATH! HUH! DOGS! I NEVER HAVE THIS BOTHER WI' JEEMY!
KHH.

OOR® WULLIE
in
"The Daytrippers!"
(Original movie 1996)

IT'S THE SCHOOL TRIP THE DAY!
WE'RE VISITIN' ROYAL DEESIDE!
STOP THE BUS!
WULLIE! OOT HERE!
JINGS! WHIT HAVE I DONE NOW?
DID YOU READ ABOUT MY ABERDEEN POLICE COLLEAGUE GIVIN' THE ROYAL PRINCES YER TIE PIN BADGES?
AYE, AN' I HOPE THEY LOOK EFTER THEM!
ON ROYAL DEESIDE....
IT'S JUST BRAW! THE RIVER DEE'S BONNIER THAN STOORIE BURN!
LET'S SEE IF I CAN GUDDLE A TROOT....
CRIVVENS! IT'S A RICHT BIG ANE....
HELP MA BOAB! IT'S A SALMON!
–AND YOU ARE A POACHER!
I SAY! IT'S WILLIAM, THE BOY ON OUR TIE PIN BADGES!
JINGS! IT'S WILLS AND HARRY!
HOME, FATHER! WE'VE A GUEST FOR TEA!
AND YOU HAVE A SALMON! YOU MUST TELL ME HOW YOU CATCH THEM!
IN THE CASTLE DINING ROOM....
THIS SALMON'S JUST BRAW! YOUR MOTHER MUST BE AS GUID A COOK AS MA....YOU MUST LET ME INVITE YOU TO TEA AN' A'!.....
BACK HAME...
THIS IS THE STUFF! MINCE FIT FOR A PRINCE!
MINCE AN' TATTIES!
JINGS! IT SMELLS DELICIOUS!
NO' A BAD DAY FOR OOR WULL AN' HARRY! HA-HA!
KEN. H. HARRISON.

OOR WULLIE in "A River Runs Through It!"
(Original movie 1992)
GONE FISHING.
I'LL CHECK MY BAIT'S A'RICHT.
BRAW LIVELY MAGGOTS!
EEK!
TIME TAE HOOK UP. TAK'S A BIT O'DOING, TOO.
TIE
DONE IT.... WHIT'S THAT DIN A' ABOOT?
SQUARK!
CHEEP! CHEEP! CHEEP! CHEEP!
SQUARK!
CLEAR AFF, YE GREEDY GANNETS!
EMPTY
BAIT
ACH! WHERE WILL I GET MAIR BAIT FRAE? I'LL HAE AN APPLE AN' THINK ABOOT IT.
A WORM! YOU'LL DO, PAL!
OCH!
I CANNA DAE IT! SLING YER HOOK.
PHEW! I'M AFF THE HOOK!
I'LL TRY GUDDLING.
CUDDLING, DID YOU SAY? ALLOW ME, WULLIE.
PRIMROSE!
YE'RE NO HOOKIN' ME! I'M AFF!
CAULD FISH!
FISH 'N' CHIPS
NAE CAULD FISH HERE I HOPE. PRIMROSE GAVE ME THE IDEA.
FISHIN' CHIPS! HO! HO!
KHH.

THE BROONS in "The Perfect Storm!"

(Original movie 2000)

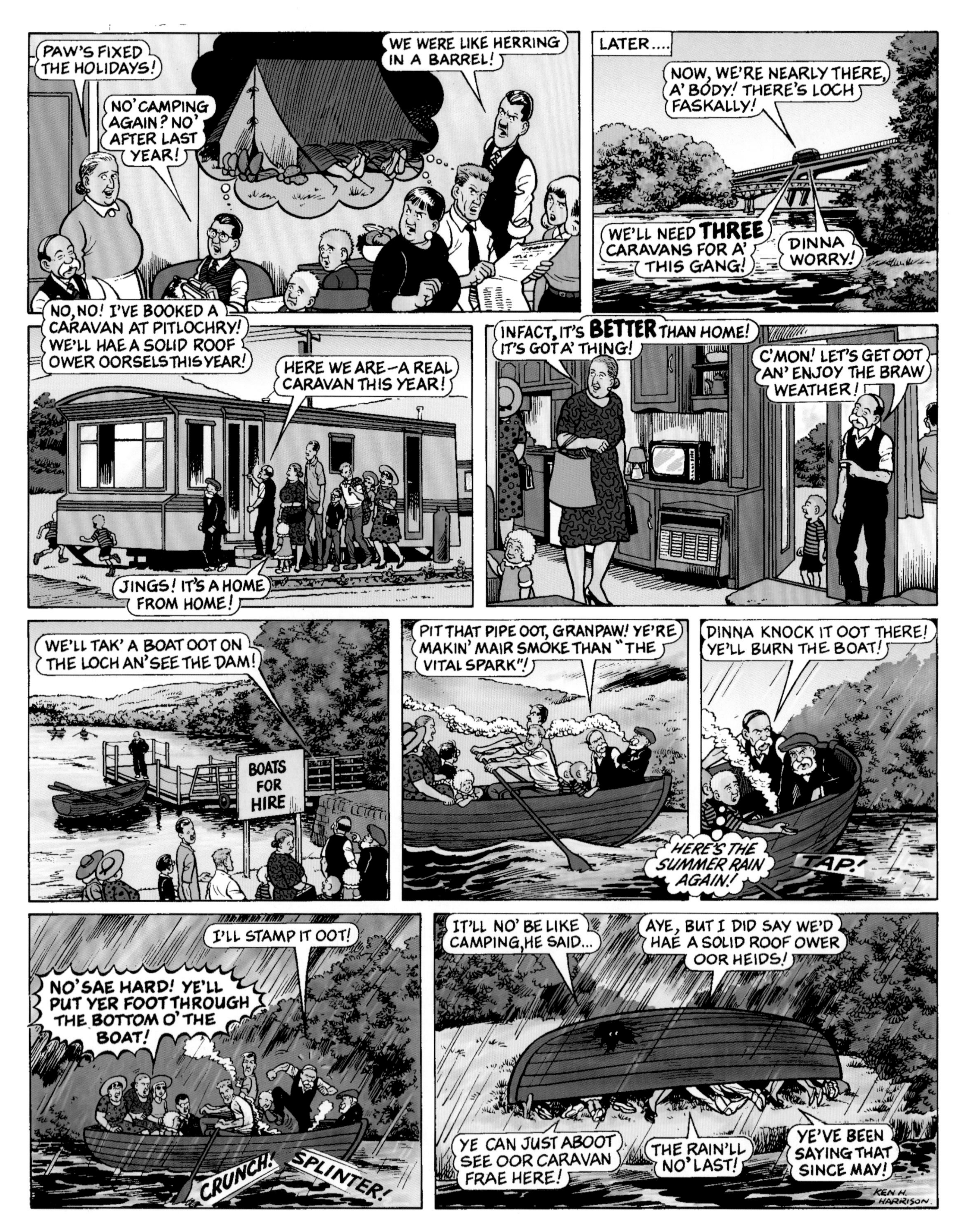

"Summer Holiday!"

(Original movie 1963)

"Rise of the Machines!"

(Original movie 2003)

in "Stakeout!"

(Original movie 1987)

WHEN IT'S NO' YOUR TURN TAE CLEAN THE
GLEBE STREET CLOSIE
Daphnie
Shuggie
STAIR
WARS

in *"Home Run!"*

(Original movie 2013)

Oor Wullie in "Gone in Sixty Seconds!"

(Original movie 2000)

OH, WOE IS ME! AH'M DOOMED!
LAST WILL AND TESTAMENT
BASHER MCKENZIE APPEARS . . .
HERE, BASHER, YOU CAN HAVE MY BEST BOXING GLOVE.
MAGIC!
HAW! WHO'S FIRST TO TRY IT OOT?
ME! EFTER A', I'VE NOTHING LEFT TAE LIVE FOR.
GROAN! CANNA LOOK.
WALLOP!
WOOF!
YE MICHT AS WELL HAVE A' MY SWEETS . . . I'LL NO' BE NEEDIN' THEM WHAUR I'M GOING.
HE DISNA KNOW WHAT HE'S DOING . . . BUT I'M NO' CARING.
AND, ECK, YOU CAN HAE THESE PLATFORMS. PRIMROSE GAVE ME FOR MY BIRTHDAY. I NEVER WORE THEM.
FOR ME? WOW!
TEA'S OOT.
I DON'T KNOW WHAT'S UP WI' WULLIE . . . BUT IT'S BRAW.
YOU CAN HAVE MY LAST SUPPER, HARRY. I'VE GONE AFF GRUB.
SLURP!
HAVE YE SEEN MY NEW CAR, WULLIE?
GULP! THIS IS IT.
INDEED I HAVE, IN FACT I'VE MORE THAN SEEN IT . . . I CANNA TELL A LIE . . . I WILL CONFESS ALL. I DROVE MY CARTIE DOON AFF THE HILL INTAE THE GARAGE . . . I DIDNA KNOW YE HAD A NEW CAR THERE . . .
WHIT'S HE OAN ABOOT?
. . . AND BELTED INTAE THE BACK O' IT . . . AND THERE'S THE RESULT . . . TWA CARS.
H-HOW?
I KEN HOW YER CAR'S IN TWA! THIS CROOK HAS BEEN WELDING AULD SCRAPPERS TOGETHER TAE MAK' ONE CAR!
IT'S A FAIR COP, GUV.
JINGS! IT'S NO' A' MY FAULT?
NO! AND THERE WILL BE A REWARD FOR HELPING TAE EXPOSE THIS ROGUE!
YE SAVED MY BACON, WULLIE. I'LL GET A NEW ANE AFF THE INSURANCE.
PAT!
I'VE GOT THE WULL TAE LIVE AGAIN. I'M FAIR STARVIN'! DINNA WORRY, HARRY, I DINNA WANT MY TEA BACK . . . WE'RE EATIN' OOT THE NICHT.
WUFF!
KEN H. HARRISON.

OOR WULLIE
in "The Long Kiss Goodnight!"
(Original movie 1996)
GLUM!
WHIT'S UP, LADS? A TRIP TAE THE DENTIST'S?
NAW! WORSE! PRIMROSE'S PARTY.
CANNA BE BAD.
ACH, IT STARTS AFF OKAY......
....PLENTY O' BRAW GRUB.....
SLABBER!
.....IF YE'RE QUICK, THAT IS! GANNET!
CHOMP! GUZZLE! SLURP!
I SAVED SOME O' GRANNIE'S HOMEMADE TOFFEES FOR YE, WULLIE.
ER....TA, PRIMROSE.
UP YE GET, LADS.... IT'S DANCING TIME!
THIS IS WHAUR IT A' GOES WRANG.... WHEN THE LASSIES TAK' OWER!
PTOO!
OCH! CANNA DANCE COS' O MY DICKIE ANKLE!
MINE AN' A'!
SAME HERE!
RIGHT! IT'S BORING DANCING WI' OORSEL'S....LET'S PLAY....
....POSTMAN'S KNOCK!
GULP! THIS IS THE WORST BIT....THE KISSIN' GAMES!
I BAGS WULLIE FIRST.... C'MON!
PULL!
DINNA WORRY, LADS. I'LL TELL HER I'M EATIN'....THAT'LL PUT HER AFF!
THEY'VE BEEN AGES... BETTER SEE WHIT'S UP.
THE BIG SAP! SEE THAT! HE'S KISSIN' HER BACK!
OOH!
MMF! YON TOFFEES STUCK US TOGETHER....COULDNAE GET AWA'! ACH! PARTIES! THEY AYE GET ME DOON IN THE MOOTH!
HA! HA!
KEN.H. HARRISON.

"Freeze Out!"

(Original movie 2005)

in "The Red Shoes!"

(Original movie 1948)

THE BROONS in "Thin Ice!"
(Original movie 2011)
THERE'S BEEN A COLD SNAP—
WE'RE AFF TAE THE BONSPIEL... THE CURLING, DOON AT SWANNEE PONDS.
WE'LL BE CURLING TAE...
...OR AT LEAST TRYIN' TO! IT'S AN AWFY FECHT TAE GET A CURL INTAE DAPHNE'S HAIR.
HA! HA!
CHEEK! AH'VE GOT A FINE HEID O' HAIR ON ME!
OCH! SEE YON GULL? GET AFF MY STANE!
IT REMINDS ME O' A JOKE I KEN.
WHIT DAE YE CALL A SCOTTISH PARROT?
WE DINNA KEN. WHIT?
A MACAW! HEE! HEE!
INSTEAD O' LISTENING TO YOUR AULD CHESTNUTS, AH'M GONNA HAVE SOME HOT CHESTNUTS. ONE POKE PLEASE.
BRAW!
WHITSAT NOISE?
MICHT HAE BEEN ANE O' MY FALSE TEETH.
CRACK!
HELP MA BOAB! THE BRAZIER'S MELTED THE ICE!
HOWL! IT'S FREEZIN'!
FSSSSS
ACH! IT'S JIST NO' FAIR! HOW'D YOU LOT GET YER HAIR TAE CURL?
CHATTER!
JIST TRY DOOKIN' IN SWANNEE PONDS AT THIS TIME O' YEAR, LASSIE! BRRRR!
HEH!
KEN. H. HARRISON.

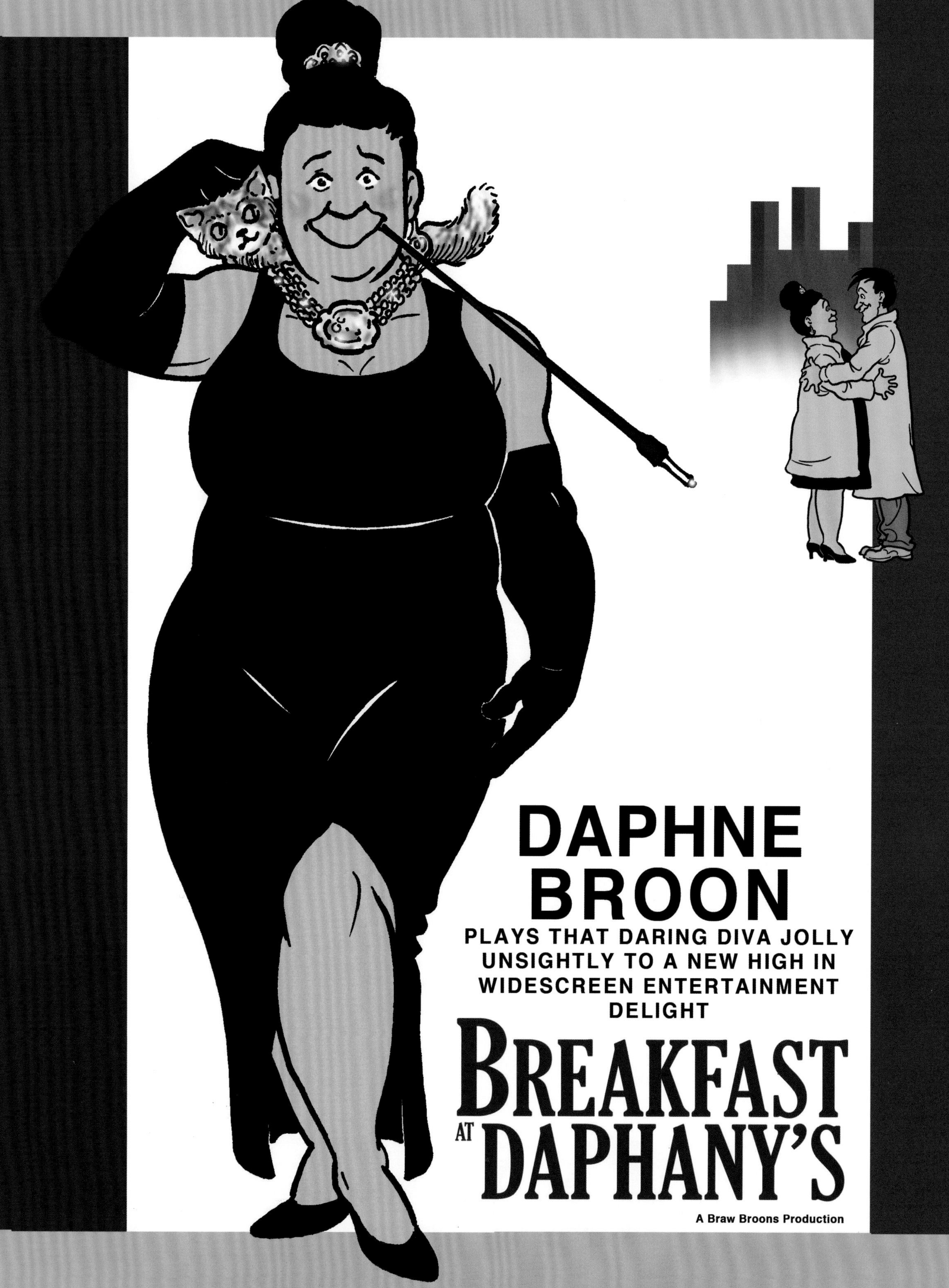

DAPHNE
BROON
PLAYS THAT DARING DIVA JOLLY UNSIGHTLY TO A NEW HIGH IN WIDESCREEN ENTERTAINMENT DELIGHT
BREAKFAST
AT
DAPHANY'S
A Braw Broons Production

Filmed on location in the Co-operative Hall, Auchentogle and behind the bike sheds in Stoorie Lane. Miss Broon's costumes were supplied by the Big Bahoochie Boutique. Tiddles the cat was borrowed from the bins beside Toni's Fish and Chip shop.

Weighting for the Summer

WITH DAPHNE BROON

Daphne's Day

On a rare hot summer's day, Daphne decided tae tak' a trip to the beach.

"Oh, man, this is braw," she sighed as she lay on her lilo on the sand. "I'll hae a dook in the watter later."

Soon she was totally relaxed and gently snoring, zzz.... zzz... zzz...

Even the gentle lapping of the water on the lilo as the tide came in didn't disturb Daphne but she was rudely awakened by excited shouts and yells from some boys close by.

"Hey, look!" cried one. "There's some auld tyres we could play wi' in the watter!"

" Naw, that's no tyres," whooped another. "It's a beached whale! Come on! Let's tak a look at it!"

"A whale!" muttered Daphne. "Michty! I'd better move. I thocht this beach was safe!"

But before she could get up, Daphne was surrounded by three inquisitive boys staring down at her.

"Aaw! It's no' a whale. It's a wifie!" said one disappointed lad.

"Sorry, missus," muttered a red-faced boy. "We thocht ye were a washed-up whale."

Daphne was flabbergasted.

"Whit, ye cheeky imps! I'll see that you're washed-up if I see yer mothers!"

The boys ran off laughing but they'd given Daphne food for thought.

"I'll hae tae dae something aboot my weight," she sighed sadly. "These wee laddies had a point."

Her day ruined, Daphne set off for home.

"Richt, I'll mak' a plan,"she decided. "First I'll throw oot my big claes so I've got to lose weight to get into smaller ones."

Daphne set to work, emptying her wardrobe and drawers. She packed everything into bags and asked her brother, Joe, to take the bags to the charity shop on his way to work.

"Nae prob, sis," he grinned, remembering he'd done this before. "Another diet, is it?"

"No," retorted Daphne, "I just need new clothes."

Some time later, Daphne made a few phone calls.

"Now I've joined a gym I'll get some exercise to help me lose weight," she thought. "And there's a bonus o' lots o' fit lads there too," she added with a smile. "Ooh, I canna wait."

That night, Daphne stepped into the gym and was immediately mesmerised by all the machines and equipment.

"Oh," she gasped. "Whaur do I start?"

Just then, a muscular young man approached.

"Is this your first time here?" he asked. "You look a bit lost."

Daphne went weak at the knees. He was so handsome! And he'd come to talk to her!! She could hardly speak.

"Aye," she stammered.

"I'm Jim," the man introduced himself, "and I can be your personal trainer, if you like."

"I'd love to," replied Daphne, blushing, "and I'm Daphne."

"Right, Daphne. We'll just take it easy for your first session," said Jim.

Soon Daphne was huffing and puffing and gasping for breath.

"If this is taking it easy what's my next session going to be like?" wondered Daphne, but Jim's lovely smile and encouragement kept her going.

Daphne happily wobbled home on legs like jelly.

"I canna wait tae tell Maggie I've got a personal trainer," she grinned, thinking of her glamorous sister. "She'll be fair jealous!"

However, The Broons' household was empty.

"A' that exercise has gi'en me an appetite," Daphne said as she helped herself to a chocolate éclair from the fridge. "Now I need to find a good diet."

And she munched her way through the éclair as she flicked through a slimming book, seemingly unaware of what she was doing.

The Broons Family was used to Daphne's diet crazes and could only watch over the next few weeks as she starved herself one minute then filled up with sticky buns and sweets the next. The novelty of Jim at the gym wore off when Maggie told Daphne that he would charge her a fortune and also that he was married. "He plays up to all the girls to get them interested enough to pay his fees," she explained.

Poor Daphne. She was fair goin' through the money she'd put aside for her new slim-size clothes, right enough. And her diet wisnae working. She'd put ON weight! What could she dae?

Daphne made a decision.

"I'll cut my losses," she told herself. "Beached whale or no', if folk canna tak' me as I am then they're no' worth bothering aboot. Now I'm off to treat masel tae a slap-up meal and then a shopping spree for new clothes....... but please dinna tell onybody whit shop I'm going into!

"Man With a Movie Camera!"

(Original movie 1929)

in *"Something Borrowed!"*

(Original movie 2011)

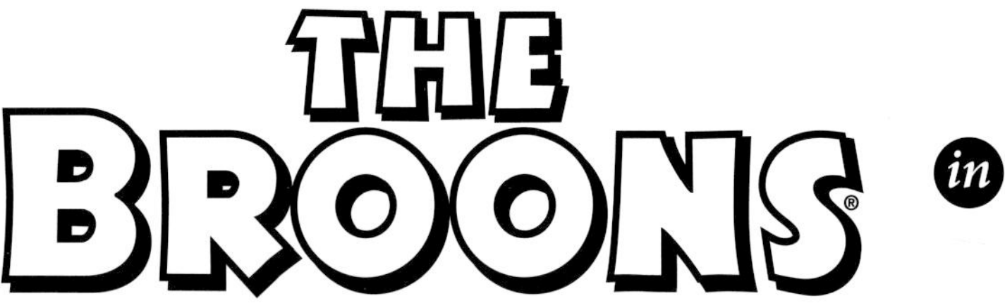

in *"The Artist!"*

(Original movie 2011)

THE BROONS in "Inherit the Wind!"

(Original movie 1960)

THE BROONS in "Gone Fishing!"
(Original movie 1997)
NEAR THE BUT AN' BEN —
MAN! IT'S A RARE DAY TAE BE OOT ON THE HILL! YE CAN SEE F'R MILES!
AYE! AN' WE'VE NEVER BEEN UP THIS BIT AFORE! BONNIE!
THIS WEE LOCHAN WID BE PERFECT FOR A SUMMER DOOK!
AN' THERE'S FISH IN IT, TAE!
THEY'LL LIKELY BE CANNY SPORT! YE'D NEED A FLY ROD TAE LAND THEM!
FLY FISHIN'? WE'VE NEVER TRIED THAT YET, PAW.
BLETHERS! I TAUGHT THE PAIR OF YE A' ABOOT FLY FISHIN' YEARS AGO! YE'VE OBVIOUSLY FORGOTTEN!
NO' TAE WORRY! I'LL SHOW YE AGAIN!
LATER —
RIGHT! ARE WE READY? GOT THE FISHING GEAR?
OCH, AYE! A'THING PACKED BUT THE KITCHEN SINK!
OOYAH! WHA'S PUT THOSE HOOKS IN THEIR BUNNET?
OH, HALF A MO'! I'VE JUST MINDED — I'VE LEFT MY REEL BACK AT THE HOOSE!
EEJIT! YE'LL HAE TAE GO BACK FOR IT!
I DINNA KEN!! YOU LADS HAE MEMORIES LIKE HENS! CAN YE NO' REMEMBER THINGS LIKE ME?
AT THE LOCHAN —
YE'RE NO' GONNA BELIEVE THIS — I'VE LEFT OOR PIECES ON THE KITCHEN TABLE!!
NOW WE NEED TAE CATCH A TROOT — OR STARVE!
WHAT A BUNCH! YE'D FORGET YER HEIDS IF THEY WERENA SCREWED ON! HONESTLY!
WHA'S THIS?
HI THERE, ALISTAIR! THESE ARE MY LADDIES — THE MAIST FORGETFUL SHOWER IN SCOTLAND! HEIDS FU' O' NONSENSE!
IS THAT A FACT? WEEL, THERE'S SOMETHING YOU'VE FORGOTTEN, BROON . . .
. . . YE'RE FISHIN' OOT O' SEASON! SO I'LL HANG ON TAE YER GEAR TILL NEXT YEAR!
HA! HA! SO MUCH FOR THE MEMORY MAN!!
SILLY AULD TROOT!
RIGHT ENOUGH! THE TROUT SEASON'S OVER!
KEN. H. HARRISON

A' THE BROONS THINK THEIR BUT AN' BEN IS...

BRAW

The Broons' Bairn

THE BROONS

The Broons' Bairn

The Broons' Bairn
THE BROONS

BOO-HOO! JOES EATIN' BUDGIES, MAW!
WHIT?
AYE — WI' ONIONS!
SURELY NO'?
HEE-HEE! IT'S NO' BUDGIES, PET — JOE'S JUST BEEN FOR AN INDIAN CARRY-OOT!
I LOVE ONION BHAJIS!

A DRAP O' CAULD TEA DOES WONDERS WI' HOOSE PLANTS!
WHIT'S THAT YER DRINKIN', PAW?
ER... CAULD TEA, PET!
MAW SAYS CAULD TEA WORKS WONDERS FIR HOOSE PLANTS!

WHAT CUDDLY TOY WILL I TAK' TAE BED WI' ME TONIGHT?
SOON-
WHAT'S THE MATTER, BAIRN?
BOO-HOO! I COULDNAE DECIDE WHAT CUDDLY TOY TAE TAK' TAE BED . . .
. . . SO I TOOK THEM ALL — AN' NOO THERE'S NAE ROOM IN THE BED FOR ME! SNIFF!

ME'LL DO THE HOOSEWORK, MAW.
FINE! THAT MEANS I CAN PUT MY FEET UP FOR A WHILE.
SUNDAY POST MAGAZINE
LATER-
WHA—? I THOCHT I WAS GETTIN' A HAND FAE THE BAIRN!
ME MEANT THE WENDY-HOOSEWORK, MAW!
SIGH! I MIGHT'VE KNOWN!

The fabulous winter scene from the cover of The Oor Wullie Book that is on sale now.
Painted by the star Oor Wullie artist, Peter Davidson.

OOR WULLIE®
in "New Year's Evil!"
(Original movie 1980)

THIS IS MY NEW YEAR'S RESOLUTION LIST.
LET'S JIST SEE IF YE'VE BEEN KEEPING THEM.
"NAE FECHTING"
HAVNAE HIT A SOUL.
TIME FOR A QUICK MUNCHIE...
UH-UH...
CHOC BAR
"...NAE EATING SWEETIES", IT SAYS HERE.
ACH!
LET ME HELP YE OOT THERE... I'LL HAE IT! HA!
SNATCH!
CHOC BAR
GIES IT BACK, YE FAT GANNET!!!
ACH! YE GREEDY WEE...
SOCK!
BIFF!
BRAW FECHT! HERE, YE DESERVE HALF O' IT, BOB.
DINNA MIND IF I DO.
SNAP!
ACH! YE'RE HOPELESS, WULLIE! THAT'S THE FIRST TWA YE'VE BROKEN ALREADY!
JINGS! WE CANNA A' BE PERFECT!
WHIT'S THIS LAST ONE?... "NAE GIRLFRIENDS"... MEANING PRIMROSE!!
HELP MA BOAB!
THAT'S ANE YE CAN KEEP, YE WEE HORROR! I WIDNAE GO OUT WI' YE IF I WIZ PAID!
PLAFF!
I'VE GOT ONE MAIR RESOLUTION...
...NAE MAIR RESOLUTIONS! WASTE O' TIME! HA! HA!
RIP!
TEAR!
KEN. H. HARRISON.

OOR WULLIE
in "The Weight!"
(Original movie 2012)

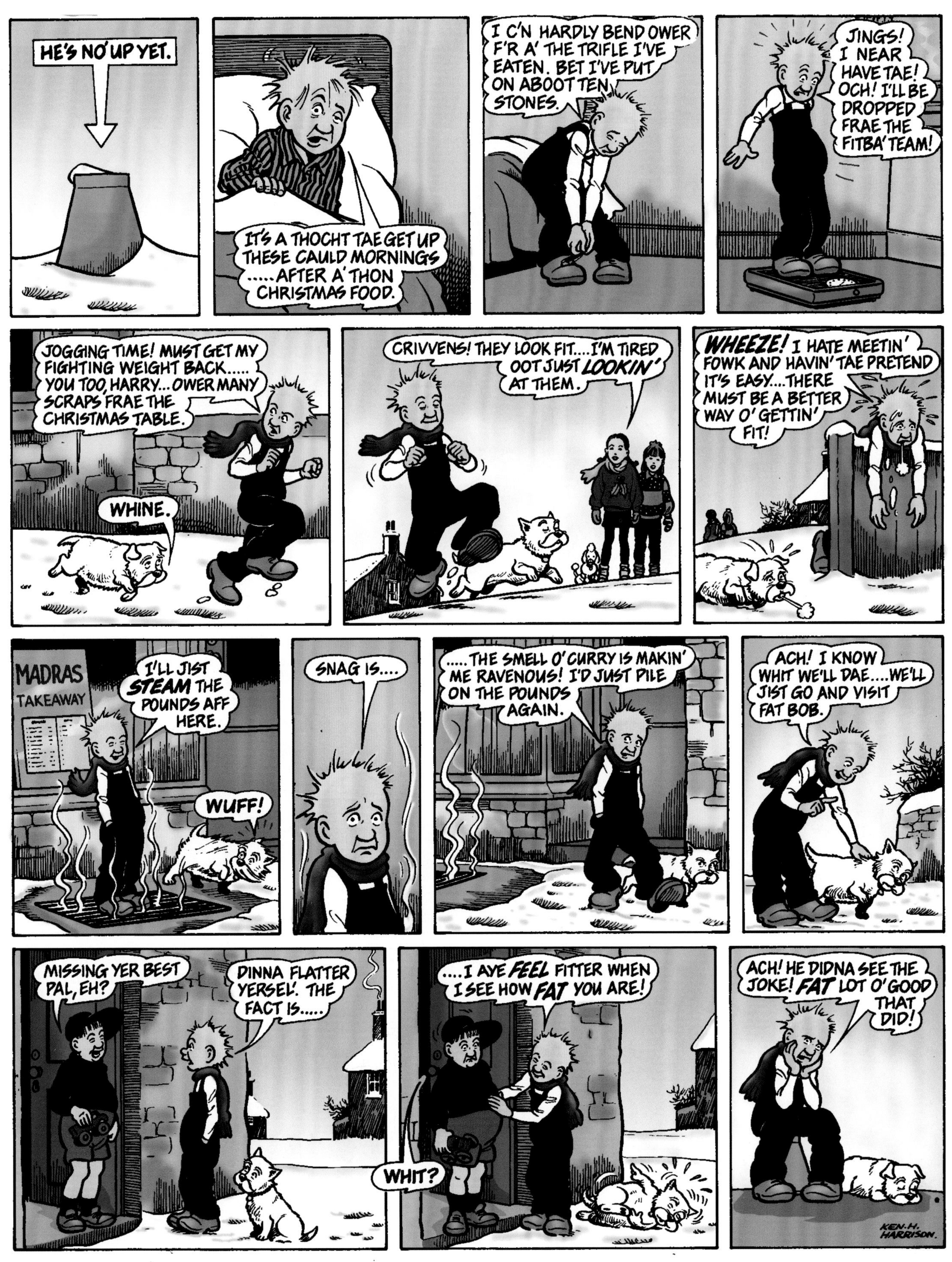
HE'S NO' UP YET.
IT'S A THOCHT TAE GET UP THESE CAULD MORNINGS .....AFTER A' THON CHRISTMAS FOOD.
I C'N HARDLY BEND OWER F'R A' THE TRIFLE I'VE EATEN. BET I'VE PUT ON ABOOT TEN STONES.
JINGS! I NEAR HAVE TAE! OCH! I'LL BE DROPPED FRAE THE FITBA' TEAM!
JOGGING TIME! MUST GET MY FIGHTING WEIGHT BACK..... YOU TOO, HARRY... OWER MANY SCRAPS FRAE THE CHRISTMAS TABLE.
WHINE.
CRIVVENS! THEY LOOK FIT....I'M TIRED OOT JUST LOOKIN' AT THEM.
WHEEZE! I HATE MEETIN' FOWK AND HAVIN' TAE PRETEND IT'S EASY....THERE MUST BE A BETTER WAY O' GETTIN' FIT!
MADRAS TAKEAWAY
I'LL JIST STEAM THE POUNDS AFF HERE.
WUFF!
SNAG IS....
.....THE SMELL O' CURRY IS MAKIN' ME RAVENOUS! I'D JUST PILE ON THE POUNDS AGAIN.
ACH! I KNOW WHIT WE'LL DAE....WE'LL JIST GO AND VISIT FAT BOB.
MISSING YER BEST PAL, EH?
DINNA FLATTER YERSEL'. THE FACT IS.....
....I AYE FEEL FITTER WHEN I SEE HOW FAT YOU ARE!
WHIT?
ACH! HE DIDNA SEE THE JOKE! FAT LOT O' GOOD THAT DID!
KEN.H. HARRISON.

OOR WULLIE
in
"The Ice Harvest!"
(Original movie 2005)

HOGMANAY TOMORROW! BRAW!
....AN' I'LL NEED A TIN O' SHORTIE, A BOTTLE O' WHISKY.... STEAK PIE... A BOTTLE OF SHERRY.....
MIND AN' GET A BOTTLE FOR ME.... A BOTTLE O' GINGER CORDIAL!
FOOD'S EXPENSIVE AN' I'M AWFY SHORT, WULLIE! YE'LL HAE T'MAK' DO WI' WHAT'S LEFT FRAE CHRISTMAS!
FLAT LEMONADE?
I'LL SAVE MA SOME CASH, THEN MAYBE I'LL GET MY BOTTLE! I'LL AWA' AN GUDDLE FOR A TROOT!
MAYBE IT'LL NO' BE SAE EASY!
THERE! JUST LIKE THE ESKIMOES!
GOT ANE ALREADY, WULLIE?
OOOH!
A' I'VE GOT ARE FROZEN FISH FINGERS!
I'LL CATCH A RABBIT INSTEAD!
MICHTY! THAT WAS QUICK!
HMM....
ACH, WHIT'S THE USE? I KENT I COULD NEVER EAT IT! COULD YOU?
JINGS! IT'S MY LUCKY DAY!
BUMP!
OH, NO IT'S NOT!
YIKES! IT AWA'!
SPLASH!
I'M GUDDLIN' FOR TURKEY!
FOR TURKEY? PAIR WULLIE! HE'S NO' WEEL!
HA-HA! WULLIE'S GOT HIS AIN BOTTLE EFTER A'!
SILLY LADDIE! YE'VE GOT A BAD CAULD! TAK' THIS MEDICINE!
MA FELT SO SORRY FOR ME, SHE BOUGHT ME CORDIAL!
HAPPY NEW YEAR!
GINGER CORDIAL
KHN.

OOR WULLIE®
in "Snowball Express!"
(Original movie 1972)

MAGIC! I LOVE THE SNA'!
BRILLIANT F'R SNA' BA' FECHTS!
JINGS! I'VE HIT MURDOCH'S BUNNET!
OCH! COME BACK HERE, LADDIES!
LATER...
MURDOCH'S LEFT HIS BUNNET LYING ...JIST WHIT I NEED F'R MY SNOWMAN.
HA! HA! THIS 'MURDOCH' CANNA CHASE ME.
WULLIE!
JINGS! HERE HE IS AGAIN... BETTER BEAT IT.
BACK HOME...
RAP!
CRIVVENS! HE MUST STILL BE BLAZIN' MAD... WHIT'LL I DAE?
WULLIE'S NO' IN THE DAY... CHEERIO.
I KNOW IT'S YOU, WULLIE... AWFY DISGUISE.
ACH! NABBED!
LOOK! I'LL COME CLEAN! IT WIZ ME... BUT I DIDNAE MEAN IT... HONEST... JIST AN UNLUCKY THROW...
I KNOW A' THAT! NAW! I WANT YOU FOR SOMETHING ELSE. BRING YER CARTIE WI' YE.
SOMETHING ELSE? OCH!
BRAW! MURDOCH'S GIVEN ME AN' MY CARTIE THE JOB O' SNOWPLOUGHING A' THE HILLS IN THE TOON!
YAP! YAP!
AYE THE MINI-SNOWPLOUGH OPERATOR'S GOT THE COLD... SO I THOCHT WULLIE AND HIS CARTIE WID MAK' THE BEST REPLACEMENTS.
SNA' BA'S... I LOVE 'EM... THESE ANES ARE FRAE MURDOCH FOR HELPING. HEH!
KEN. H. HARRISON.

(Original movie 2009)

OOR WULLIE

in "The Jacket!"
(Original movie 2005)

IT'S RIGHT CAULD THESE DAYS. YOU COULD DO WI' A NEW JACKET, WULLIE!
WE'LL TRY THE SALES!
BONNINGTONS CLIM
SALE
SALE
THERE'S BRAW JACKETS IN THE NEW HIGH ST. CLIMBING SHOPS!
IT'S LIKE WEARIN' A HOT WATER BOTTLE!
IT'S THE LATEST THERMAL, ALU-LINED, POLAR ZERO PLUS—
—AND IT'S ONLY £180!
IT REALLY IS A BRAW JACKET....
....EVEN THE PRICE HAS RAISED MA'S TEMPERATURE!
MAYBE WE'LL GET SOMETHING MAIR REASONABLE IN HERE.
WHA'S NEXT
HOW'S THAT, SIR?
40
HAVE YE ONYTHING SMALLER?
IT MAKES SIR LOOK RATHER PUBLIC SCHOOL!
PUBLIC FOOL MAYBE!
WHA'S NEXT?
SALE RAIL
40
SO THAT'S HOW THE SHOP GOT ITS NAME!
THIS LOOKS MAIR LIKE THE THING!
ARMY SURPLUS STORES
PARKAS
DUFFEL COATS
COMBAT SOX
AND THE PRICE IS RIGHT!
IT'S NO' EXACTLY NEW!
THAT'LL DAE YE NICELY!
COMBAT GLOVE
SALE
DUFFEL
NICE T' GET HAME! IT'S FREEZIN'!
THE HEATING'S AFF!
I HAD T' GET THE PLUMBER! WE NEED A NEW JACKET FOR THE WATER TANK!
I HAVE JUST THE THING!
A PERFECT FIT!
WHA NEEDS A JACKET ONYWAY— THEY'RE FOR AULD FOWK!

OOR WULLIE
in "The Bed Sitting Room!"
(Original movie 1969)

THE NICHTS ARE FREEZIN' JUST NOW — I NEED A 'HOTTIE' FOR MY BED!
AN EXTRA BLANKET OR TWA DOES A LOT O' GUID, TOO!
BUT THEN
FLOP!
HOWL!
JINGS! WHIT'S THAT?
OOT! THIS IS MY BED — YOUR BED'S OWER THERE!
OCH! I'M ONLY WEE — YE'D NEVER KNOW I WAS HERE!
SOON
BOY! THIS IS GREAT!
THEN
WHEESHT, HARRY! YOU'VE GOT AN ON-BOARD FUR COAT! ARE YE A DOG OR A MOOSE?
CHATTER!
TH-THAT'S EASY F-FOR HIM T-TAE S-SAY!
MIND YOU, IT DOESNA TAKE LONG TAE GET AWFY WARM UNDER A' THESE COVERS!
BUT I'M NO' TAKIN' ANY COVERS AFF — I'LL OPEN THE WINDAE A WEE BIT INSTEAD!
WHIT???
OH-OH! ER . . . GOOD BOY, HARRY! I WIS ONLY JOKIN'!
WOOF! WOOF!
HERE! WHIT ARE YE DAEIN', HARRY?
GRRRRRR!
WHA—? HARRY! YE CANNA BE SERIOUS!
PULL!
AND
HUH! IT'S A DOG'S LIFE, IS IT NO'?
ZZZZZ!
NEXT MORNING
MAN'S BEST FRIEND? SHEESH!
KEN. H. HARRISON.

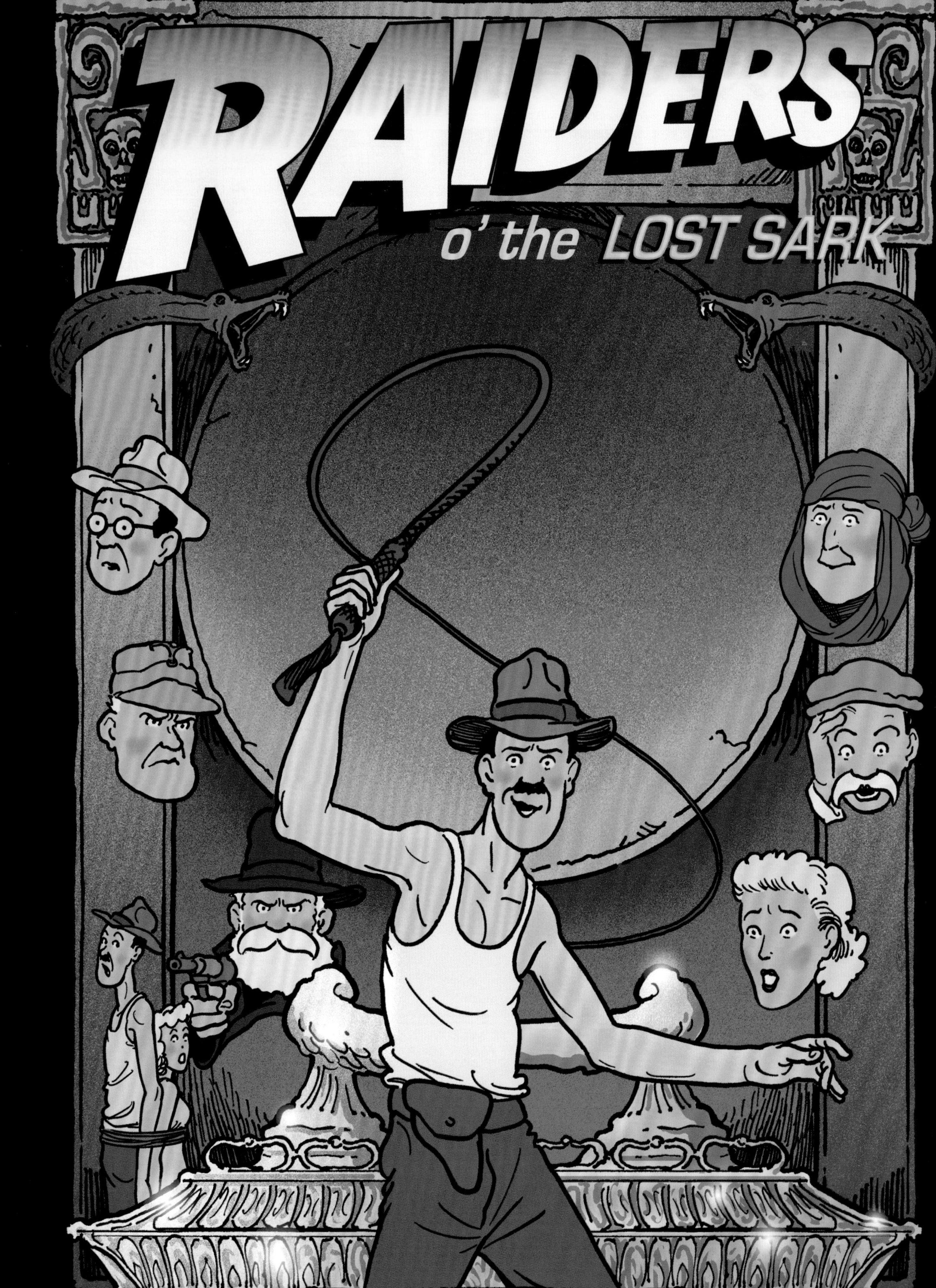
RAIDERS
o' the LOST SARK

THE BROONS
in "Cop out!"
(Original movie 2010)

MICHTY! THERE'S A POLICE CAR DRAWIN' UP AT THE DOOR! WHIT'S GOIN' ON HERE?
IT'LL BE NOTHIN' TAE DAE WI' US, MAW!
POLICE
OH, THE SHAME! IT'S YER FAITHER! WHIT'S HE BEEN DAEIN'?
PAW BROON!!
DINNA STRUGGLE, BROON!
HANDCUFFED? WHAT HAVE YE BEEN UP TAE?
OH, THE DISGRACE!
JINGS! A' THE NEIGHBOURS ARE LOVIN' THIS!
FAINT!
I WIZ...ER... SHOPLIFTIN'...
IN A MANNER O' SPEAKING, HE WIZ INDEED!
OCH! THAT'S DISGRACEFUL!
I THOUGHT YE WERE HELPIN' OOT AT THE BAIRNS' PAIRTY?
THAT'S JUST IT-WE WERE!
...MURDOCH AN' MASEL' WERE SHIFTIN' SOME O' THE TOYS...
IT'S HEAVY, THIS ANE!
CLARK'S FUDGE
...AN' THE BAIRN WAS INSIDE...
SWEETIE SHOPPE
HILL'S MINT LUMP BARS
CLICK!
"SHOPLIFTIN'", EH? YE'RE NICKED!
...AN' THE KEYS TAE HER HANDCUFFS ARE IN THE TOYBOX IN HER ROOM.
HA-HA!
YE WEE MONKEY! YE'VE MADE US A LAUGHIN' STOCK! COME HERE!
A LAUGHIN' STOCK? HUH! THAT'S NO' DIFFICULT!
RARE FUN!
LET'S GET OOT O' HERE, BROON!
KEN.H. HARRISON.

THE BROONS in "The Railway Children!"

(Original movie 1970)

in *"Fiddler on the Roof!"*

(Original movie 1971)

THE BROONS
in "Empire of the Sun!"
(Original movie 1987)

AT THE BUT 'N' BEN–
MY! WHIT A BRAW DAY FOR TOASTING!
HAW! HAW! JUST LOOK AT PAW! WHIT A SIGHT!
YE'LL A' BE SORRY WHEN YE'RE BURNT TAE A CRISP!
I'M AWA' FOR A WALK!
IT IS AWFY WARM. I'LL HAE A WEE SUNBATHE.
I DINNA WANT THE FAMILY TAE SEE ME.
STICK ON BAGS O' SUN OIL SO'S I DINNAE GET SUNBURNT. I BROUGHT THIS BOTTLE FRAE THE HOOSE.
MAN, THIS IS BRAW!
ENOUGH FOR ONE DAY. DINNA WANT SUN-STROKE. ONYBODY SEEN PAW?
HERE HE COMES NOO!
HELP! I CANNA MOVE!
YE SILLY AULD GOWK. THAT'S SUNFLOWER OIL, FOR COOKING! YE'VE DONE YERSEL' TAE A TURN!
PAW BROON? MAIR LIKE WULL SCARLET!
KHH.

THE BROONS in "Other People's Money!"

(Original movie 1991)

SO YE THING IT'S EASY MAKING A FULL COLOUR BOOK? WELL, GET YER PAINTS, PENS OR PENCILS OOT AND TRY YER HAND AT COLOURING IN THE NEXT TWO SCENES. ANE SHOWS THE LOCH NESS MONSTER AND THE OTHER SPRING CLEANING AT KELVINGROVE MUSEUM. GOOD LUCK AND TAK' YER TIME!
Wullie's Shed

ROCK NESS
TV

MONSTER
LOLLIES

KELVIN
ELEPHANT
MAIN HALL
NO. 247.
TOOTHP
SENSIT

RT GALLERY AND MUSEUM
GORAI

ROXY